# Crack Cocaine
# The Open Door

# Crack Cocaine
# The Open Door

**Christopher Robin**
**Kenneth Jordan**

**Janus Publications**

*This book is dedicated to all those whose lives have been affected by crack cocaine.*

*GOOD LUCK!*

# *Contents*

# Acknowledgements

I would like to thank those who have positively influenced me and who have enabled and encouraged me in the co-writing of this book. They begin with my mother Vernice Evelyn Robinson, who allowed me the forum to express myself. My wife Jennifer Jordan (my backbone) who simply says 'go for it and don't spend too much time looking back'. Malieka Robinson, my sister, who taught me through her actions in life, to never stand still. And David Hoy, my professional mentor who encouraged my learning in the drugs field and is one of the most humble men I know!

**Kenneth Jordan**

I would like to thank my children, whom I love dearly. Darius, Keighley, Naomi, Brandi and Rio, who have helped me to develop my communication skills. Also my mother Angela Joseph who has always had faith in me. My brother Derek, and my sisters Lucy, Maryanne, and Loretta, who always seem to be proud of me no matter what I do. My mentor Eric Rodney, who taught me that in order to communicate with a client, I would have to acquire a bag of tools. And last but not least to my girlfriend Mary Bell, who has always told me that I need to take ownership for who I am, and has always given me 110% support to achieve my goals.

**Christopher Robin**

# *FOREWORD*

The problem of drug dependency, like the poor 'who are always with us', has historically dogged the footsteps of successive governments. Despite concerted periodic attempts to help this service user group, outcomes have continued to be disappointing, nothing seems to work and a reliably effective method of intervention and service provision has yet to be established.   The implications of drug dependency for society are far reaching: they impinge on all our major institutions, the Criminal Justice System, mental health services, education, employment, housing and the NHS. Most importantly, drug dependency causes untold human misery and suffering to the users themselves and to everyone who is involved with them: their parents, partners, children, extended families and their friends.

Despite the usual minority of detractors who oppose any vanguard of social reform there has been enormous good will from all sections of society and a real commitment to understanding drug dependency and to promote attitude change from a position of dismissive condemnation to one of 'these people are in need and deserve, and are entitled to help.'   But with no increase in success rates and the problem of drug dependency showing no sign of abating, an insidious and unwitting culture of hopelessness has crept into our consciousness.   There has been a gradual drift towards perceiving drug dependency as an 'intractable problem' and then locating the 'intractable problem' in the drug user.   The person, the drug user themselves, by osmosis then <u>becomes</u> the 'intractable problem.' And so the vicious circle of 'failed' service users in conjunction with 'failing' service provision continues to beat its well worn path of self-perpetuating negative expectation.

In 'The Open Door' Janus Solutions describe how they have developed a different model of intervention, which has been tried and tested over a period of years. They argue their case with a refreshing vigour and conviction born out of careful observation, much heartsearching, scrupulous self-examination and productive reflection.

Centring on the crack cocaine user and the 'intractable' problem of crack cocaine use as the focus, this much needed book cuts through the veneer of ideologies to the heart of service failure endemic in this area of service provision. By refusing to accept that the crack cocaine user presents an intractable problem to the drugs professional and unpicking the dynamics of the drugs professional's interaction with the service user, Janus discovered a subtext of hidden agendas, mutual misunderstanding and false assumption. On the surface the professional is conscientiously adhering to all the precepts of good practice – seeing the person not as the problem, valuing and respecting the service user and applying a needs-led, task centred approach to negotiating the support plan. But it is the subtext of unconscious processes which actually drives the relationship between drugs professional and crack cocaine service user and undermines the genuine belief on the part of the service user that the professional believes in them and can help them, and undermines the professional's genuine belief in the services user's motivation.

10

Janus Solutions explain how drugs professionals can develop a new and more potent awareness of these hidden dynamics and then explain it to the service user. They clarify confusion about key concepts such as motivation, resistance and diversity. They teach us how to ask more relevant questions and how to listen effectively so that further questions and information-sharing expand mutuality, awareness, empowerment and a support plan which enables the service user to tackle his/her real issues.

'The Open Door' is not afraid to discuss the sensitive issue of the drugs professional's contribution to the hidden agendas of their relationship with their service users, or to explore the thoughts and feelings of both professional and service user which are so often left unsaid but which hang in the air between them and manifest themselves in non-verbal communication through body language or tone of voice. These unspoken messages destroy trust and damage the potential for realistic hope and positive progress.

The message of this book is that what is sauce for the goose is sauce for the gander and that what we expect of our service users we should also and equally expect of ourselves, our colleagues, our teams, our policy makers and our umbrella organisations. 'The Open Door' is a courageous book, immensely readable and informative and essential reading for all health and social care professionals. Janus Solutions are not asking the reader to do anything which they have not already asked of themselves and therein lies their integrity.

**Mary Lettington, Consultant Social Work Trainer**

# *Introduction*

When we decided to write this book, we first considered our personal experience of crack cocaine training in the early 1990's. We did not recall the training as a positive experience in particular, as the information being delivered was confusing, and the trainer had very little experience of working directly with crack cocaine service users. The majority of the training was spent looking at the history and the pharmacology of the drug. When we then found ourselves in front of a client, it was hard to imagine how it might help them to know that cocaine was found in an Egyptian tomb many, many years ago! At a more recent training event we found once again that the facilitator spent a lot of time focusing on the pharmacological impact of crack cocaine on the user, leaving little or no time to focus on the **engagement** of the crack cocaine service user – an aspect that we felt should surely be the priority. The immediate thought that came to mind was how little that crack cocaine training had changed over the years.

The professional needs to examine how he or she individually works with this particular service user group. Janus Solutions feels that the professional should not be presented solely with historical and/or pharmacological information, which in fact can be easily accessed, on the Internet for example. The skill of working with the crack cocaine user, or any drug user, is to be able to translate theory into practice. As the authors we have eighteen and fourteen years experience respectively in the drugs field and have endeavoured to write a book that is a true reflection of how we as professionals have worked with the crack cocaine service user. We also worked as crack cocaine specialist workers, and have co-ordinated and developed crack cocaine programmes both separately and together. The questions this book asks of you, the reader, the drugs professional, represents the questions we the authors, ask ourselves as professionals working with adults and young people who have a dependent relationship with crack cocaine.

Janus Solutions made the decision to write this book because there are no books that focus on working with the crack cocaine service user. We wanted to provide a forum to ask questions of our services and practices, and to stop blaming the crack cocaine client for our own inadequacies, because after all, they do what they have always done, and that is to take crack cocaine. We believe that it is time to look at ourselves, because only through this process can we then make the necessary changes.

The book covers many topics, some of which we felt have created obstacles in working with this service user group. Examples of this are: how we can work with this service user if there is no awareness of diversity, and how can we expect a client to get to know him or herself, but do no work with them around their cravings?

We called the book the 'Open Door', because we believe that the practitioners' awareness primarily of themselves in their practice, is the key to developing services that are accessible to crack cocaine users. This book aims to develop the practitioners' self-awareness and challenge their pre-conceptions in order to open the door to this client group, and facilitate informed choice and opportunities for positive growth and change.

Open discussion is essential to increase understanding of most things within society, and people's use of substances is no exception. If we as professionals view ourselves as trail blazers then we should be able to ask honest and challenging questions of ourselves and the services and organisations that we work for. Included within this are policy leads and strategists. The crack cocaine user has presented us with an opportunity to ask ourselves some soul-searching questions. If as professionals we have perceived the crack cocaine user in a negative way or have used our powerful role to mask our discomfort, this will underpin our intervention. These factors have influenced the culture of approach towards crack users and the types of treatment or service offered, so that the outcomes are poor and yet the quest for evidence based research, so often sought in other areas of the drug field, are only reflected in criminal justice statistics with this client group.

The current political demand for evidence based research precludes all distribution of resources and notably few resources appear in our communities for crack and cocaine users. If services are to be developed based on the present day currency, then research can take place that identifies the needs of the crack cocaine user. This research must encompass all aspects of the user not only one part, such as their criminality.

Evidence based research could consider some of the following questions in order to get a fuller picture to inform practice.

14

- What can we learn from the last 25 years of the crack cocaine service users' experience of services?
- On what evidence base are the proposed interventions to stand?
- Why are psycho-social interventions harder to define and 'evidence' than prescribing interventions?
- Why do we need to label the crack cocaine user in order to categorise him eg. with mental health diagnostics?
- Why do we expect crack cocaine users to be aggressive and violent and how does this influence our expectations and responses to them?
- Why do we perceive the crack cocaine user to be more difficult to treat than other drug users?
- Why do crack cocaine users know little or nothing of drug services until, perhaps after many years of using, they come to know of services through detention within criminal justice system?
- Is there a role for pharmacological interventions for primary crack cocaine users?

The list goes on. However, what is more important than the length of the list is whether we have failed these service users in the past, and are failing them now. With crack cocaine there is a superb opportunity for all open-minded professionals to learn and not to repeat the same mistakes as with other drug users. Janus Solutions believes that in many ways, primary crack cocaine users are often the easiest clients to work with.

**Why is that?**

Because we believe that the practitioner's task is to engage the client and the only obstacle to this lies within ourselves. In this book we invite the practitioner to take a new look at their practice and to open themselves to the possibility of enhancing their professional and personal development.

# *Chapter One*

## Pharmacology

### What is dependency?

*'....a syndrome in which the individual continues to take the drug because*
*of the pleasurable effects which are derived from it.  This behaviour occurs*
*despite the adverse social or medical consequences which it may have.'*

(Brian E Leonard: Fundamentals of Psycho-pharmacology (2nd Edition))

### What is pharmacology?

*'The science of drugs, chemical agents that affect living processes.'*

(Encyclopaedia  Britannica 15th addition)

### What is Crack?

Crack is a smokeable form of cocaine.  It is not a special substance that in some mythical way transcends cocaine powder, it is simply cocaine hydrochloride (cocaine powder) that has been treated with either ammonia or sodium bicarbonate (baking soda) and heated to remove the salt (hydrochloride). Note: this does not in any way minimise the impact of this drug on the individual however, it is essential to stress the fact that we are talking about a smokable form of cocaine.

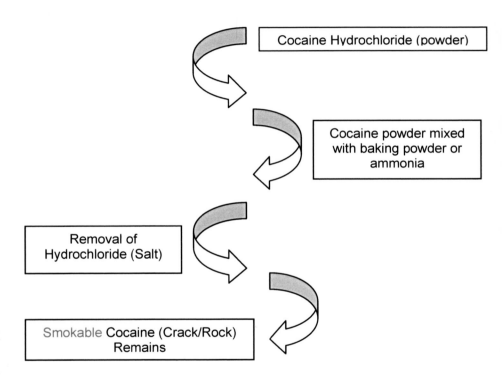

The hydrochloride form of cocaine is water-soluble making it excellent for nasal use and intravenous use. Cocaine base is insoluble in water making it less suitable for snorting and injecting and more suitable for smoking. However, some cocaine users do smoke cocaine hydrochloride (powder) and clearly identify a 'high'

18

with that form of using the drug, hence the 'high' experienced by the cocaine powder smoker should not be dismissed, even though it may not, necessarily, be the most 'efficient' way of using and ingesting it.

**Why smoke cocaine (crack)?**

Snorting cocaine has certain limitations as to how much of the substance can be absorbed into the system, as the surface area of the membrane within the nose is small. (It should be noted that the blood vessels within the nose will also constrict, limiting the speed with which the drug enters the blood stream). For cocaine powder users who are out of control of their snorting, damage to the nose would be a natural outcome of over use.

If someone smokes cocaine then the cocaine will have access to most of the lungs. This area is far larger than the nasal area allowing more gaseous cocaine to enter the blood stream. The red blood cells (erythrocytes) then carry the respiratory gases to the brain. Naturally this happens within seconds, hence the famous 'high' the crack cocaine service user describes.

*A thought!*

When we describe the high of crack cocaine we often say that it is more intense than, snorting, or smoking cocaine powder, or eating the drug etc. However, we need to pay attention to the type of 'buzz' or 'high' the individual likes or wishes to experience. Also the type of physical feeling someone becomes used to, i.e. the stinging nose and watery eye of the snorter, and the resulting sensation after that or, sitting on a chair and taking a deep pull on the pipe, and the sensation that follows.  People have:

- Particular habits and
- Enjoy particular sensations

And this needs to be recognised and stored in our collective computer, otherwise we will only be looking out for the 'pipe smoking crack user'.  This would be incorrect!   Always be mindful of the many ways in which crack cocaine may be ingested.

### What dictates a 'high'?

### An exploration of Pharmacokinetics and Pharmaco-dynamics

These are concepts that are part of the language of pharmacology but are often unknown even to substance misuse professionals. They should be remembered and considered as a kind of 'rule of thumb'.  There is a reason why drugs give off a powerful effect when they enter the body.  Processes take place and these processes are what professionals work with all the time.  At times we might not be mindful of the full implications of what is happening and why the drug user, in this case the cocaine users of both 'powder' and 'rock', are going through what they are going through.

Unfortunately some vital pieces of information are locked away within the minds of particular professionals, when in fact they should be disseminated across the whole field, enlightening professionals from all backgrounds as to what we are dealing with when we are talking

20

about an individual's relationship with their drug or drugs of choice. This is something that service users need to understand also, in a palatable language of course, to give them more understanding of their relationship with cocaine.

## Pharmacokinetics

What happens when a drug enters an organism, in this case the human body?

Remember, pharmacology is the study of how substances interact with living organisms to produce a change in the function of the organism. Pharmacokinetics is concerned with the rate and extent of:

- **absorption** of a substance into the body
- **distribution** of a substance throughout the body
- **metabolism** of the drug within the body
- **excretion** of the substance from the body

*In simple terms, for the cocaine user, the **speed** with which the drug enters the blood stream and the **amount/quantity** of the drug entering the system are the **crucial components** of the 'high' someone experiences.*

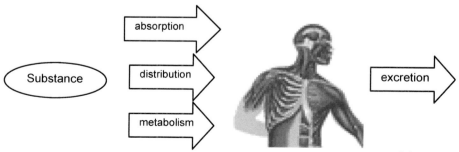

Note: if the drug cannot be **excreted** from the system, it can build up bringing harmful effects with it. Also toxicity can take place, either through a build up of the substance or through chemical processes occuring within the body through a particular type of drug use. This is often the foundation of the health issues associated with drug use! An example of this is the combination of cocaine and alcohol, which forms cocaethylene. This can lead to greater chances of cardiovascular toxicity in the body and ultimately, sudden death. Note: this is the exception, and not the rule!

The aforementioned is the basic reason we encourage someone to both use **smaller quantities** of the drug as well as encouraging them to use the drug in such a way as to **prevent so much** of it entering the blood stream at one time.

**Pharmacodynamics**

Pharmacodynamics introduces the idea that drug use is not solely about what the drug does to the body (i.e. pharmacokinetics), it also focusses on what the body does to the drug (pharmacodynamics). This shows us that drug use is a two way process, a relationship which says that someone's physiological and cellular make-up influences the nature of the impact a drug has on that individual.

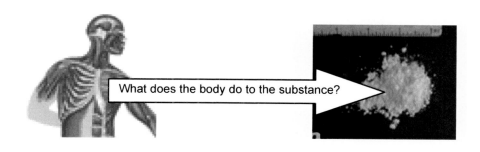

What does the body do to the substance?

Pharmacokinetics and pharmacodynamics work in tandem; much like cravings and triggers, one is intricately woven into the other. The two neurotransmitters associated with cocaine i.e. dopamine and seratonin demonstrate this two way process well. Note: this process applies to the use of all substances.

**Neuro Transmitters: Dopamine and Seratonin**

**Dopamine**

When the 'high' of cocaine is mentioned dopamine is mentioned. Why?

*Researchers have discovered that, when a rewarding event is occurring, it is accompanied by a large increase in the amounts of dopamine released by neurons. In the normal communication process, dopamine is released by a neuron into the synapse (the small gap between two neurons), where it binds with specialized proteins (called dopamine receptors) on the neighbouring neuron, thereby sending a signal to that neuron. Cocaine is able to interfere with this normal communication process. For example, scientists have discovered that cocaine blocks the removal of dopamine from*

the synapse, resulting in an accumulation of dopamine. This buildup of dopamine causes the continuous stimulation of the receiving neurons, which is associated with the euphoria commonly reported by cocaine users.
(NIDA 2007)

**Serotonin**

In the <u>central nervous system</u>, serotonin is a neurotransmitter which is believed to play an important role in the regulation of <u>anger</u>, <u>aggression</u>, <u>body temperature</u>, <u>mood</u>, <u>sleep</u>, <u>vomiting</u>, <u>sexuality</u>, <u>appetite</u> etc. Low levels of serotonin may be associated with several disorders, namely an increase in aggressive and angry behaviours, <u>clinical depression</u>, <u>obsessive-compulsive disorder</u>, <u>bipolar disorder</u>, <u>anxiety disorders</u> etc.
(Wikipedia 2007)

For whatever reason, the aforementioned role of serotonin within the body changes and influences the re-uptake of dopamine into the system. This in turn influences the 'low feeling' or 'crash' that the cocaine user subsequently experiences.

Note: many cocaine users may present to General Practitioners (G.P.'s), long before accessing services. When they present to their G.P. their symptoms may well mirror depression of one form or another. If the G.P. is unaware that the service user has a cocaine problem, s/he may prescribe a serotonin based anti-depressant that may create more difficulties if the cocaine user uses cocaine on top of the medication. It is important for drugs professionals and G.P.'s

24

to create learning relationships with one another and within the community to ensure that the service user receives an appropriate intervention as opposed to a reactive intervention.

**The role of Pharmaco-therapies for the crack cocaine user!**

No pharmaco-therapies have yet been developed for the treatment of cocaine users (Fox. B 1997) and as such alternative interventions are essential. Leading neuro-theorists such as Volkow, Wang, Fowler et al (1999) carried out studies trying to identify the association between drug cravings for the cocaine user, and the right orbital cortex and the right striatum. Their investigations were inconclusive. The **National Institute on Drug Abuse** (NIDA) identified the development of a pharmacological treatment as its top priority. It is clear that a pharmacological intervention is a goal within many institutions dealing with treatment and research, however, Carroll et al (1994) while investigating effective long term pharmaco-therapies in the treatment of cocaine dependence could only conclude that, as yet, there are no long term pharmacological interventions available.

The reason this has been mentioned at the earliest possible stage of this discussion, is because there are no drug based treatments for crack cocaine service users as yet! NIDA in America, are clear that a pharmaco-therapy that can either block or reduce the desire of someone to use the drug is its number one priority. Even though there are trials taking place, at the present time there is no standardised drug based treatment.

**Does Cocaine (Crack) affect the service user psychologically or physically?**

When reading about cocaine or talking to professionals about cocaine and its effect on the human organism, there appears to be a consensus that cocaine affects people on a psychological level and that it is solely a *psychological drug*. For a drugs professional this is an important discussion point because crack/cocaine users often present to services:

- Not understanding what is happening to them on a physical and emotional level, not to mention understanding their own mental state.

*Let us remove the myth that crack/cocaine users present to services as 'the expert'. They are not the expert of their own condition; if they were, they would not require so much of 'our' insight. It would probably be more appropriate to say that the drugs professional has not given this subject matter enough thought and consideration!*

If at the point of engagement we make *statements* to the service user and those *statements* do not gel with what the service user is experiencing then we may appear to be a *'professional fool'* in the eyes of the service user. This is an important point because crack/cocaine does have a physical impact on the service user as well as a psychological impact, and it is essential as a drugs professional to listen and explore with the service user, how the drug affects them physically.

26

It is important that we do not view the physical impact of cocaine in the same way that we view **alcohol** and **opiate** physical dependency. We must flex our intelligence in a more **lateral way** rather than from a rigid perspective, in other words:

### cocaine is a psychological drug!

**An example of this is the impact of cocaine on the release of adrenalin throughout the body.**

*Adrenaline is a "fight or flight" hormone which is released from the adrenal glands when danger threatens or in an emergency. When secreted into the bloodstream, it rapidly prepares the body for action in emergency situations. The hormone boosts the supply of oxygen and glucose to the brain and muscles, while suppressing other non-emergency bodily processes (digestion in particular).*

*Adrenaline plays a central role in the short-term stress reaction—the physiological response to threatening, exciting, or environmental stressor conditions such as high noise levels or bright light. It is secreted by the adrenal medulla. When released into the bloodstream, epinephrine binds to multiple receptors and has numerous effects throughout the body. It increases heart rate and stroke volume, dilates the pupils, and constricts arterioles in the skin and gut while dilating arterioles in leg muscles. It elevates the blood sugar level by increasing catalysis of glycogen to glucose in the liver, and at the same time begins the breakdown of lipids in fat cells. Like*

27

*some other stress hormones, epinephrine has a suppressive effect on the <u>immune system</u>.*

*Although epinephrine does not have any psychoactive effects, stress or arousal also releases <u>norepinephrine</u> in the brain. Norepinephrine has similar actions in the body, but is also psychoactive.*

*(Wikipedia 2007)*

The definition above makes a powerful statement about the impact of the release of the hormone adrenalin into the system. It makes mention at the end of definition that it "does not have any psychoactive effects." Consider then the **physical** and **psychological** implications of having a prolonged exposure to adrenalin, that goes a long way beyond the normal length of time when the hormone is released in everyday stressful situations.

### The service user mentions feeling:

'Wired'! What would it feel like to you to have adrenalin pumping round your system for 10 minutes, 20 minutes, 1 hour? What would it feel like to have adrenalin running around your body for that length of time?

Again we ask the question, can crack/cocaine lead to a psychological or a physical dependency? Also, have we given enough thought as to how we should diseminate this information between one another as professionals, and to the service user?

This suggests there are gaps in knowledge and information used by workers in the provision of services for this client group. We need to re-evaluate how we engaged this client group in the past and how we might want to develop our knowledge base in order to better engage with them now.

# *Chapter Two*

# The Jo-hari Window

**To operate a service without regularly reflecting on the culture and nature of:**

- **where you work**
- **how you work and**
- **the culture and history of your work environment,**

**would be poor practice**.

However it is not easy to explore operational processes in depth without a guiding model or contextual framework and for a service to put itself under the microscope, a certain amount of courage is required. The Jo-hari Window is a model that offers an interesting and helpful perspective on the client, the professional and the service.

**4 ways of using the Jo-hari Window**

The Jo-hari Window is a flexible tool, which allows the service user, the professional and the team to learn about awareness 'together'. We will explore:

1. The Jo-hari Window model
2. The clashing of the service users' Jo-hari Window and the professionals' Jo-hari Window
3. The Jo-hari Window: the Service User, the Professional and the Service
4. The Jo-hari Window and the crack cocaine user

## 1. What is the Jo-hari window?

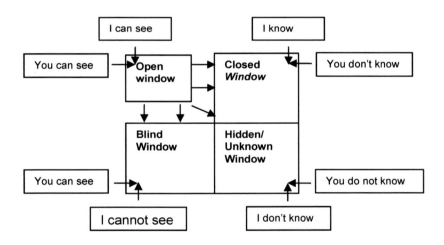

The Jo-hari Window identifies 4 aspects to a human being. These aspects ultimately represent how an individual behaves and reacts with regards to themselves, others and situations. It is sometimes viewed by professionals as a simplistic tool, but we have found that it is an effective framework which is particularly helpful when working within the substance misuse field.

**The Windows**

**The Open Window:** represents those things that the individual concerned is aware of and feels comfortable with. It also represents something that the outside world (friends, family, work colleagues etc.) is aware of. There are no surprises in this window for all concerned, for example: *'I have black hair* I am aware of that, I have black hair and feel comfortable with it and you are aware that I have black hair and you are comfortable with it.' There are no surprises!

**The Blind Window:** represents things within the individual, that they show the world, that they are **not** aware of. However, those on the outside (family, friends, work colleagues etc) *can* see it and are aware of it. In drugs counselling, it is from this window that we ask questions, for example:

**Drug Counsellor:** *May I say something?*
**Service User:** *Yes*
**Drug Counsellor:** *I've observed when you talk about giving up crack/cocaine, you smile. Were you aware that you do that?*
**Service User:** *No I wasn't*
**Drug Counsellor:** *That's my observation ..........*

**Service User:** *Oh!*

**Remember:** *The aim of using the Jo-hari Window is to open wider the window of self-awareness within the client/service user. The blind window is the most useful window for the drugs counsellor because it is the window, from which we ask questions, based on* **our observations!**

**The Hidden or Unknown Window:** represents things about the individual which he/she is not aware of and neither is the outside world of friends, family and work colleagues etc. Behaviour is nonetheless still affected by this unknown 'stuff' although as yet no-one knows what it is, or even that it exists. This is the unknown, the unconscious and the sub-conscious. The hidden or unknown window is also associated with skills and attributes that an individual has, but may not be aware of. We seek to be mindful of hidden strengths as well as limitations. For example:

*'When I was young I was very good at football, I particularly enjoyed playing the game with my friends. I really enjoyed being part of a team, and actually on reflection I was the captain because* **I was a good leader'**.

**The Closed Window:** represents what the individual is aware of, what s/he knows about themselves, but what friends, family and work colleagues etc. are **not** aware of and do not know. 'My behaviour is affected by what I and I alone know about myself that I am not yet ready to admit to or talk about'. If the information that is kept to oneself is unhealthy, then issues may result from this window. This is

34

sometimes called the window that houses **secrets!** Fear, shame and guilt can all at times be found within this window.

**Remember:** *All the windows affect human behaviour, and at times the windows overlap, but we should proceed with great caution, and only after discussion in supervision, before attempting to open the closed or hidden windows with a service user. Because we do not know what will come up, or what can of worms might be opened. Particular skills may be needed to deal with the emotional fallout of exposing these two windows and if those skills or appropriate support structures are not available, the consequences could well be catastrophic for the service user.*

## 2. The clashing of the service users' Jo-hari Window and the professionals' Jo-hari Window

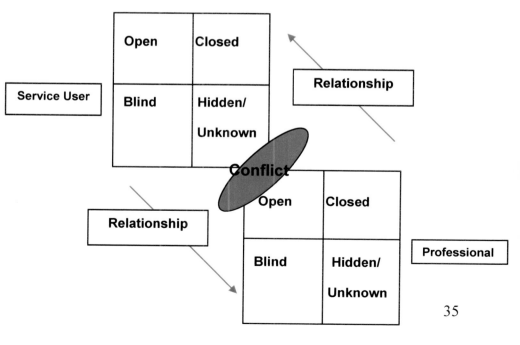

35

**The service-user:** it is expected, and it is accepted, that he or she will have an open side, a blind side, a closed and a hidden/unknown side to their persona. We explore and aim to discover crucial traits within the client that influence his or her relationship with a drug. Naturally, we also gauge our relationship with the service user, taking for granted that he or she will exhibit behaviour to us. For example, if the professional is of a particular gender, sexuality, race, size, apparent intellect, sensitivity, is an ex-drug user or presents a paternal or maternal nature etc., all these aspects will influence the service user's relationship with that professional. We often use therapeutic expressions like:

- Projections
- Transference

The Jo-hari Window offers the professional the opportunity to explore the service user, and is also a tool that can be directly offered to the service user as a means of developing **independent** self awareness.

The next question is, does the **Professional,** being human, operate within the Jo-hari framework? As professionals, we must assume that we exist within the context of being:

- **open** and aware of particular aspects of ourselves;
- **blind** to our own actions and behaviour as professionals, accepting that others, including service users, can see and recognise very clearly who we are;

- **closed** around certain specific issues and experiences that have fundamentally shaped who we are as people, as well as having a
- **hidden** side, which comprises such deeply hidden feelings and experiences that we are unaware of them.

Rather than using expressions such as **Counter Transference,** let us instead ask the question:

'What happens when two Jo-hari Windows clash, that of the client and that of the worker?'

*Answer:*
*A dynamic relationship that can be full of silent and covert conflict*

## 3. The Jo-hari Window, the Service User, the Professional and the Service

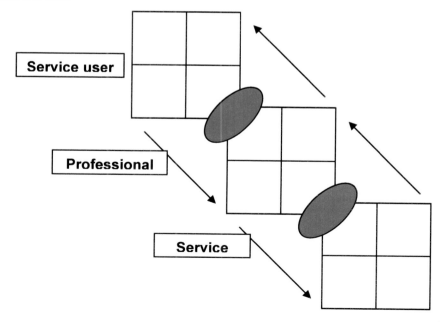

By extending the use of the Jo-hari Window to the professional, and then further extending it to the actual service and the type of treatment that the service offers, the Jo-hari Window provides an opportunity to explore service development. This is particularly relevant to identifying and changing the culture of the work environment to meet community needs in relation to specific drugs. The culture, which exists within a team and a service is akin to the blind and closed windows. Only through a service asking itself relevant and pertinent questions can it respond appropriately to change and changing needs. An obvious example has been the lack of appropriate service response to crack cocaine users.

It is essential that we explore the client, the professional and the service in a dynamic way. We must, in order to make our services as appropriate and effective as possible, analyse critically what we do, and what we do and do not offer service users. To have a framework to explore the above is essential as, all too often, we do not recognise the importance of:

- Clinical Practice
- Supervision and Appraisal
- Service Development opportunities etc.

This entire discussion should encourage a team and service to explore and enhance its open window of awareness, by referring to its blind window and constantly asking itself questions such as:

➢ *Why are we not engaging crack cocaine users in an area where there is high crack use?*

38

**Consider:** What happens when the Jo-hari Window of the client, clashes with the Jo-hari window of the professional, which then clashes with the Jo-hari Window of the service?

## 4. The Jo-hari Window and the crack cocaine user

The Jo-hari Window provides an excellent framework for approaching the crack cocaine user. It is a framework that is easily added to the drug professional's tool bag. A drugs professional's major focus with the service user is the individual's use of and relationship to their drug of choice. The service user needs to be encouraged to be receptive to constant questions and observations from professionals. On occasion professionals allow themselves to be pushed and pulled by the service user from one climactic situation to the next. Professionals often call this the client's:

### *'CHAOTIC LIFESTYLE'*

Crack cocaine users are often viewed as 'chaotic', however, as professionals we may need to explore with the service user and the team;

*What do we mean by 'chaotic lifestyle? What is the service user's investment in chaos? Is there any such thing as chaos in reality?*

It is essential for the drugs professional to realise that their fundamental relationship with the service user is to create understanding within the client, about his or her relationship with drugs. If a professional becomes bogged down in being a:

- Housing Officer
- Doctor
- Psychotherapist
- Family Therapist etc.

then their skill base may be stretched. There is a recognition that the above needs to be done, but not always at the behest of the service user. Drugs professionals must enhance their skills around drug counselling and be absolutely clear about their role and task.

The most appropriate treatment for crack cocaine users is talking interventions. The consequence of this is that the drugs professional must develop far ranging and extensive communication skills, which both challenge and encourage the crack cocaine service user to explore themselves. It may be noted that complementary therapies and pharmaco-therapies have not been mentioned here because first and foremost our ability to talk to the crack cocaine user is at the very root of effective intervention.

| Open | Closed |
|---|---|
| | |

| **Blind** | **Unknown/** |
|---|---|
| <ul><li>When have you ever used only one stone?</li><li>How are your cravings today?</li><li>Are you aware of how crack cocaine works?</li><li>What does boredom mean to you?</li></ul> | **Hidden** |

The drugs professional should be aware that when they ask questions in this window it may initially put the client on the defensive, but the professional still has the responsibility to ask these questions. The skill lies in the effective use of asking questions and making observations. No matter the work environment the service user should realise that they are communicating with a drugs professional. The blind window may lead to the service user becoming more aware of their closed and hidden windows because any question or observation may trigger a powerful reaction. However the objective of the drugs professional is to keep the service user aware of their goal regarding their drug use.

**As a framework**

The Jo-hari Window is not a sophisticated work tool that requires the professional to undertake years of training in order to establish a reliable working knowledge. It is a tool that, if you allow your imagination to expand, can be used in:

- 1:1 client work
- Group work
- As a relapse and lapse self questioning tool for the service user
- Staff supervision
- Team Meetings
- Team Building days and Away days
- Service Development
- Needs assessments
- The list goes on.....

One of the most fascinating aspects of this model is its ability to bring together the service user, the professional and the culture and ethos of the service environment, to identify the areas of difficulty and to then find more effective ways of working together. The ability to ask the correct questions at the right time is crucial; unfortunately in order to achieve this we have to empty the excess baggage from the hidden and closed windows.

# *Chapter Three*

## What is Resistance?

*The story of the frog and the scorpion:*

*A scorpion wished to cross the river, however he could not swim.
'How can I get across that water?' he asked himself. The scorpion
looked around, and his eyes fell upon a frog sheltering in a bush.
'Take me across the water frog!' The scorpion said.
'Not on your life!' The frog replied. The frog was no fool. 'If I take
you, you will surely sting me!'
'Don't be silly frog! If I were to do that, we would both die!' The
scorpion was aghast.
The frog considered the scorpion's argument, and it made sense. He
could flip the scorpion off his back when they reached the other side
of the water. So the frog agreed realising that he was in control of the
situation.
'Hop on my back,' said the frog to the scorpion.
The scorpion did as he was told and the frog set off and everything
was fine until he felt the most excruciating pain penetrate his back.
He arched his back in agony and raised his head and looked upon
the scorpion. Realising he was dying he said with his final words,
'We are but half way across the water! We will both die! Why, why did
you do this scorpion?'
The scorpion looking down upon him replied simply,*

## 'It's my nature!'

Service users can view themselves in a very singular way, as can the professional, much like the scorpion. If the service user and the professional view the drug user as an addict, a junkie, suffering a sickness etc, then it could be argued that the client and the professional have a limited perception of what the client can achieve, through a belief in what the client is. When working with a client around change it is important to be mindful of not only the language that is used, but also the culture of the environment that is created around the service user.

As professionals we often reflect that the client is 'resistant'. The client is struggling with change, is struggling with the idea, for whatever reasons, of taking on new behaviour and ways of being. What is this inability to change, to take on different ways of being?

If we explore the idea of attributes in relation to a service user, i.e. *qualities intrinsic, inherent and naturally belonging to a thing or person,* our aim should be to encourage the development of attributes and qualities which will be helpful to the service user in achieving the goals identified in their treatment process. (Note: these are not necessarily spiritual or moral but simply 'aspects' of an individual, such as humour). It is helpful to view these attributes as muscles; some muscles or attributes we exercise a lot, other attributes or muscles we exercise rarely, therefore they are far less developed and as a result less functional. Our object is clear. It is to support the service user to develop attributes or muscles, which will aid them in achieving their goals.

However something called *resistance* gets in the way. This *resistance* takes many forms, and can have a huge emotional impact on the professional who is working with a service user. It can also manifests itself in a variety of ways. As professionals it is important to give *resistance* a shape and a form so that we have a clear picture of what we are dealing with. It is also important for all professionals to construct a mental and emotional framework around *resistance*:

**The Bereavement Chart**

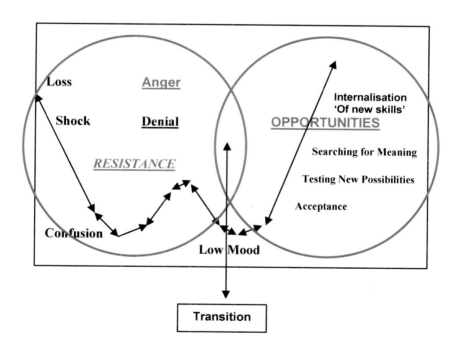

From the bereavement chart we are able to create a framework to explore what *resistance means* for drug users looking to change their behaviour and relationship to their drug of choice.

***This chart identifies resistance as:***

- **Loss**: the harm or privation resulting from losing or being separated from something or someone
- **Shock**: A sudden or violent disturbance to one's mental or emotional faculties
- **Confusion**: A state of being confused mentally, a lack of certainty, orderly thought, or power to distinguish, choose or act decisively
- **Denial**: A refusal to accept or acknowledge the reality or validity of a thing or idea (you need to stop using drugs!)
- **Low Mood**: A predominant emotion. Note: The term 'depression' is avoided because it should only to be used when appropriate, not as a matter of course, with the crack cocaine service user
- **Anger**: A reaction to the above. It may take different forms i.e. an outward physical expression of not wanting to change; a simmering silence which repels advice and support when the subject of change becomes a real part of the drug session; witty responses to questions or statements too *close to the mark* etc. These could also be classified as defence mechanisms.

This suggests that resistance is the melding of the above into one powerful force, which presents an obstacle to both the service user who believes that s/he wishes to change their relationship with crack cocaine, and the professional who encounters this obstacle 'resistance'.

An important type of resistance is the conforming service user, who is apparently the model client, but who quickly begins using drugs or alcohol as soon as they have completed their *treatment*. In this situation all the professionals may well have been side tracked because they were probably not aware of the nature of the resistance, *either their own or the service user's*.

All too often when we work with the service user we pay attention to the *OPPORTUNITIES* aspect of the chart i.e.:

- Acceptance
- Testing New Possibilities
- The Search for Meaning
- The Internalisation (*of new skills*)

We omit to pay attention to *resistance,* or we have not created a framework, that provides us with a context for what *resistance* really means. This chart is a way of viewing why, and in what circumstance, service users may be resistant to change or new ways of being. Note: in order to look at *resistance* it is important to remember that this is not always about the service user, it can also be about the professional and the culture of the treatment environment.

**The team**

Is resistance solely the responsibility of the service user? No.

This is the case for a very simple reason. Generally we should expect the service user to present with an aspect of themselves striving for change, while the other aspect of the service user desires to remain the same, enjoying the 'taste' of their drug of choice, and the associated behaviours of that drug use.

Remember someone often changes when they come into contact with a particular type of:

The *obstacle* has a profound and thoughtful impact on the service user forcing them to reconsider what and why they are doing something, in this case using *crack cocaine*. It is probably important to remember that it might not be the most obvious thing that encourages someone to explore and experiment with the idea of transition and change, and then further explore the idea of resistance within themselves. So a service user saying:

- 'I want my children back' may not be a changing force within the service user.
- 'I hate my mum'. This kind of admission may not be the correct stimulus for an individual to explore change.

- 'My partner uses but I want to give up'. A co-dependent relation is not the easiest place from which to contemplate change.

As professionals when we work with resistance our reference point comes from

- Our own life experiences
- Our training

As a team we usually have quite different life experiences and come from a variety of professional backgrounds with different types of training credentials. Therefore as an individual worker and as a team, the varying perceptions of resistance can be problematic and cause conflict. If we explore the reasons for resistance from different theoretical perspectives we can get some insight into how teams mismanage the resistance within a service user and its impact on the service user's relationship to change.

### *How differing theoretical perspectives approach resistance*

### <u>Psychodynamic Counselling</u>

**A psychodynamic framework** may focus on historical traumas that may have had a powerful impact on the service user. These traumas may have been rooted in childhood, or have evolved in unhealthy relationships that have impacted greatly on the individual. Often the practice of a psycho-dynamically trained therapist is to be neutral, interpretative and non-directive. For these practitioners, drug use is a symptom of deep-rooted, entrenched issues.

> ***How a psychodynamic therapist may manage resistance:*** *The therapist may take the position that the service user will discover in their own time, and through self processing, how to navigate change, and better understand their own personal resistance through a process of self discovery.*

## Operant Conditioning

**Operant Conditioning** and the Criminal Justice System: Those practitioners operating within a criminal justice framework may work with the service user in a variety of ways, however they may use positive and negative reinforcement:

- In **Positive Reinforcement** a particular behaviour is strengthened by the consequence of experiencing a positive condition. For example:

  - A crack cocaine user takes part in the interventions offered within the Criminal Justice System (CJS). They are compliant, are listening, engage in treatment options and using educational resources etc. As a result of this behaviour, which fits within the parameters of the CJS, the service user receives **rewards.**

- In **Negative Reinforcement** a particular behaviour is strengthened by the consequence of stopping or avoiding a known negative condition. For example:

□ The crack cocaine user acts out behaviour that goes against the rules of the Criminal Justice System. The result of these actions is a negative response to the service user by the CJS eg. going to jail. The service user realises that if s/he offers the 'system' what it wants then s/he can avoid the negative response from the 'system'. The service user realises that the more s/he conforms to the needs of the Criminal Justice System the more positive rewards s/he will receive.

*How a Criminal Justice Worker may manage resistance:*

*A criminal justice worker may view resistance within a service user as an indicator that a service user is unable to re-access society or if they do, they will soon return to criminal behaviour. Resistance within the service user is something that has to be overcome using varying degrees of* **pressure/incentives**

## Motivational Interviewing

The **Motivational Theorists** may see their role as one that builds upon the service user's internal resources. Using a directional tool kit the MI theorist creates a platform whereby the service user must explore their need to change entrenched behaviour. The worker might ask questions about another area of the service users life in order to draw comparisons in the process of change:

**Therapist:** 'You feel that you no longer enjoy crack?'

**Service user:** 'No I don't!'

**Therapist:** 'So you wish to stop?'

**Service User:** 'Yes!'

**Therapist:** 'However you are still using crack?

**Service user:** 'Yes'

**Therapist:** 'Is there a type of food you do not like?'

**Service user:** 'Milk!' (A little confusion at the question)

**Therapist:** 'So you drink milk?'

**Service User:** 'Of course not!'

**Therapist:** 'So you do not drink milk because you do not like it?'

**Service User:** 'Of course not!'

**Therapist:** 'So you enjoy crack!'

**Service User:** 'Crack isn't milk!'


The service user is angry, but more importantly at that moment the service user is incongruent with their drug use, i.e. s/he is made uncomfortable due to the type of directional/manipulative questioning they received.


I do not drink **milk** because I do not like it!

I say that I no longer like **crack cocaine**, yet I still smoke!

**How the Motivational Interviewer may manage resistance:**

*The MI practitioner may view resistance as perfectly normal, recognise that the service user may return to drug use on more than one occasion and that lapse and relapse are an accepted part of the process of a service user achieving his or her goal.*

## Cognitive Behavioural Therapy

The **CBT practitioner** will encourage the drug user to realise that their acquisition and use of crack cocaine are not random spontaneous actions over which they have no control. The worker will, through the use of techniques and exercises, encourage the drug user to explore the journey from the point of having no drugs in their possession to the point of using crack cocaine. The CBT practitioner will present the service user with rationales that they use to justify his/her drugs seeking behaviour, and ultimately his/her drug using eg.

### Once won't hurt!

By this means, the service user's false logic 'justifies' using drugs, in this case crack cocaine.

*How the CBT practitioner may manage resistance:*
*The CBT practitioner may believe that the service user is unable to process cognitively their drug using behaviour in a different way and is at this moment unable to take on new cognitive skills when the problem is actually one of resistance.*

There are many theoretical perspectives, these 4 merely demonstrate the point that different perspectives work with and interpret transition and the resistance that comes with it in very different ways. The same can be applied to how professionals with their own life experiences, or services with their own ethos and cultures, work with the transition and resistance that a service user

53

may experience.  Both the practitioner and the service user will have a rationale that makes sense to them regarding resistance.  The difference can often lead to misunderstanding and conflict between individual practitioners, services and service users that can ultimately jeopardise the potential benefits that a service user stands to gain from a service.

**Resistance as a Survival Mechanism**

If we explore resistance to change as a survival mechanism, even though it is not always the case, we can see why the crack cocaine user holds onto the desire to use the drug.  Where the theorists and drugs professionals may come into conflict is in their failure to recognise that 'drug counselling' is not CBT, Behavioural Psychology, Motivational Interviewing, Freudian Psychology, Psychiatry, Nursing, 'I am an ex-user!', Gestalt etc.

Drug Counselling could be described as bringing the service user to a place whereby they own that they love the 'high' and the behaviour associated with crack cocaine use.  There may be deeper issues; they may have trauma; they may have their children in care; they may be in co-dependent relationships; they may have lost their job, they may have lost their families, etc. however, the focus of the drug professional's work is their relationship to crack cocaine.  The service users 'resistance' to address their dependence will be individual to them so in order for the drugs worker and the team to get the best possible outcome for the service user, they must also acknowledge that they as professionals are individually in a state of resistance, that often manifests itself in the form of conflict.

54

### Two aspect of Resistance

Resistance has two core aspects:

- The service user
- The worker/service

In order to maximise the service user's potential for coming to terms with the change they are looking to achieve i.e. to reduce their crack use, stop their crack use or use crack more safely, they have to be offered a space within their treatment to recognise that in the process of transition and change, they will resist the process that they appeared to be entering into 'willingly'.

However the process of resistance also encompasses the worker and the service. When faced with the clients' needs, the worker, the team and the service may also have to change or adapt. There must be an agreement reached by the whole team to engage in this process if the goal is to be achieved that leads to the best possible outcome for the service user.

The crack cocaine user provides an example of a service user group that has been misunderstood on all levels. The drugs professional has to keep the drug at the heart of the work they carry out with the service user. Confusion over role prevents the appropriate exploration of resistance within the client.

How many people who enjoy their behaviour, whether or not it is to their detriment, change for no apparent reason? And if resistance is a part of what a person goes through when confronted with the prospect of change, why as professionals do we not include resistance as fundamental to the interventions that we offer the service user?

# *Chapter Four*

## Motivation

Motivation is a vast and complex subject, yet it is one that drugs professionals use in a matter of fact way. As drugs professionals we need to bear that complexity in mind and achieve clarity about the impact of motivational theory on, and within, the framework of operational service provision to drug users. Most importantly we need to understand the framework both as individuals and as members of a team.

Motivation is frequently mentioned in all types of treatment interventions to do with substance use i.e.:

- the service user must identify what motivation means to them!
- the drugs professional must be a catalyst for the service user to get in touch with their own internal motivational resources.

If the service user is not motivated then no positive change can take place resulting in the service user either not making progress towards the identified goals around their drug use or their drug use remaining the same.

## What is Motivation?

## Motivational Theories

Because motivation is such a vast field we need to explore some motivational concepts to show us the full breadth of what stimulates our desire to do or not do something. Remember this is an area that should be explored by the professional, and discussed within a team, in order to identify some degree of consensus around the service user and his/her 'motivation'.

### *Motivational Concepts:*

|  | Definition |
|---|---|
| Reward and Reinforcer | A **reward** is that which follows an occurrence of a specific behaviour with the intention of acknowledging the behaviour in a positive way.<br><br>A **reinforcer** is different from reward, in that **the reinforcement** is intended to create a **measured rate of increase** in the desirable behaviour **following the addition of something** to the environment. |
| Intrinsic and Extrinsic Motivation | **Intrinsic motivation** is evident when people engage in an activity for its own sake, without some obvious external incentive being present. A hobby is a typical example. |

|  | *External motivation is the result of applying some external 'force.' An example would be a 'bonus' or 'positive feedback' which stimulates affirmative action in, for example, your job.* |
|---|---|
| Punishment | *Punishment is using something that is not 'pleasant' to get rid of actions or behaviour that are seen as being 'wrong' or 'undesirable'.* |
| Aggression | *Aggression is the use of force to achieve a goal.* |
| Stress | *Stress and feeling under pressure may trigger a feeling of 'underachieving' that actually motivates someone to perform and achieve (reverse psychology). Therefore stress can motivate someone into action.*<br><br>*Bear in mind that there are 2 types of stress: Eustress and Distress. Eustress refers to good or helpful stress. Distress represents the opposite of that, and there is something of 'suffering' attached to it.* |
| Secondary goals | *There are primary type motivations that operate around the need to survive and procreate as well as motivations that are more indirect such as getting money or a bonus, for your work. Note: the indirect motivator or the secondary goal can* |

| | |
|---|---|
| | become very powerful, and may even eclipse the primary survival/procreative type of motivation. For example, 'personal image' can become so important that it disrupts normal eating patterns leading to a potentially destructive eating disorder. Using drugs and/or alcohol is another obvious example. |
| Coercion | **Coercion** is getting someone or something to behave in a particular way through the use of an external force. The desired outcome is that the individual will give back 'something.' That 'something' could be labour, or their power, their will etc. |
| Self Control | **Self Control** refers to someone exercising their self control to achieve a particular goal. This is somewhat different to responding to a drive or desire to eat food, which is driven through a biological need. |

The above illustrates some forms of motivation, and even though individuals may identify with some of the above more than others, it may be wise to say that all of them have some meaning to us. When a drugs professional is exploring motivation: 'How motivated are you Mr/s Drug User to change aspects of your life' we need to be clear in our own minds as to what 'motivation' means.

## Why is someone 'motivated' to use drugs?

Is it unreasonable to say that the reason someone is motivated to use crack cocaine or any substance is because it influences how the individual:

### Thinks! Feels! and Behaves?

When someone uses a drug, whether they enjoy it from the very beginning, or whether they learn over a period of time to enjoy it, they have a 'motivation' to use for that enjoyment. How important is it to say that the individual has a physical connection/addiction with the drug or an emotional connection/addiction to the drug? When we view the substance in such an 'immense way' i.e. that 'crack' is an all powerful substance, a professional can feel powerless by believing deep down that the drug user is beyond change. As professionals we know that something that affects the way an individual thinks, feels and behaves is a powerful motivator, which is the reason they continue using a drug for a long period of time. This suggests that the crack cocaine user requires a **very good reason to change.** Note: re-entering mainstream society may not be a good enough motivation.

How responsible is it for the drugs professional to suggest that a service user should re-enter society on our terms, when in fact they are deliberately avoiding the 'real' world? How responsible is it to suggest to the service user that they will enjoy the 'real' world? Note: the suggestion here is not that we should **not** take the service user on a journey of change in relation to their drug use but that the drugs professional should carefully plan the journey so that it encompasses the service user's real fears and actual motivation. When we sit down with a service user we tend to look at motivation from our own perspective. For example: 'If you go out and get a job your life will be better.' But this is an assumption that is not necessarily true for this person. Re-entering the world of work in mainstream society may not only increase that person's anxiety but may also **inescapably remind them of their lack of lifeskills and coping skills.** Some service users will probably be aware that not only would getting a job not make their lives better but that it might also make their lives much worse. The drugs professional must be aware of what each service user may encounter on the journey and at the end of the journey, and negotiate a plan that is tailored to that individual's needs and motivation.

In such a situation, where the service user is indeed aware that the advice being given is not going to be helpful in the context of their lives and their drug use, we might expect the service user to simply say to their worker: 'But I don't think that is going to help me because a job is going to make me even more stressed out and I'll use more in order to cope.' However this tends not to happen and there are two reasons for the service user's silence:

- The service user may feel constrained to pretend to agree with the drug worker and say only what they think their worker wants to hear.
- The service user is afraid that if s/he does not follow their drug worker's advice they will be criticised and accused of 'lacking motivation.'

That is the reason why, when we explore motivation with the service user, we should be careful not to create **incongruence** for them and always to monitor our practice for assumptions that may well be false.

**Consider!**

**How many times have we heard a service user say:**

- I have to stop using drugs because I want my children back
- The relationship with X is abusive I need to leave him/her
- We cannot stay together because it's a using relationship
- I cannot afford to go back to prison!

If the service user does not achieve their goal they may:

- Lose their children
- Maintain that abusive relationship
- Carry on using with their partner
- Get sentenced and return to prison once more!

The drugs professional's feelings can be so affected by the fear of the outcome, that they forget that the service user's motivation to use crack cocaine was to affect the way s/he thinks, feels and behaves, and **that** motivation was greater than, for example, their concern for their own children.

**The question is: Why is that the case?**

### The Parable of the Hole in the Road:

*On the first day... a man walks down a street...*
*Suddenly the world goes dark. He thinks he is lost.*
*Then he realises he is in a deep hole. He tries to find his way out,*
*and it takes a very long time. Once he is out the day is gone ... so he*
*walks back home.*

*On the second day... the man walks down the same street.*
*The world goes dark again. He is in the hole again.*
*He takes a while to recognise where he is. Eventually he finds his*
*way out... and so again he walks back home.*

*On the third day... the man again walks down the street.*
*He knows the hole is there and pretends not to see the hole... and*
*closes his eyes.*
*Once again he falls into the hole, and climbs out ... and walks back*
*home, the day lost once again.*

*On the fourth day... the man walks cautiously down the street.*
*He sees the hole and this time walks around it. He is pleased.*
*But the world goes dark again. He has fallen into another hole.*
*He climbs out of the second hole, walks home ... and alas... falls into*
*the first hole. He gets out of the first hole... and walks back home...*
*to think.*

*On the fifth day... the man walks confidently down the street.*
*He sees the first hole..... and recognises it.*
*He walks around it... but forgets the second hole, which he walks*

*directly into. He gets out immediately... and walks straight back home - to weep and hope.*

*On the sixth day... the man walks nervously down the street... The hole is there and he thinks "I won't fall into the hole again"... and walks around the hole. He sees the second hole, avoids the second hole... but as he passes, he loses his balance... and falls in. Climbing out he walks back home ... taking the time to carefully avoid all the holes. On the seventh day... the same man goes for a walk....*

**... and chooses to walk down a different street.**

# Motivation:

**how it applies to the drug user?**

*The interesting thing about the parable is how the man copes with an 'obstacle'.*

Motivation as a wide ranging subject matter requires some thought and consideration according to the context. The interesting thing about the above parable is the process the man went through. However in order to explore this further lets introduce a stage **before** day one.

Generally we know that the service users motivation to use a drug competes against everything else, and lets call 'everything else', life responsibilities. That stage **before day one** is:

# I really enjoy using drugs!  There is no competition!

|  | Parable | The Crack Cocaine Service User |
|---|---|---|
|  | **Before Day 1**: I use crack cocaine and I love it! ||
| **Day 1** | *On the first day... a man walks down a street... Suddenly the world goes dark. He thinks he is lost.* ............................ | *One day after using the man realises that as well as the **pleasure** of using crack the using is bringing problems in to his life regarding work and his family.* |
| **Day 2** | *On the second day... the man walks down the same street.* *The world goes dark again*............ | The second day after using the man realises that his life has changed considerably since he began using drugs. |
| **Day 3** | *On the third day... the man again walks down the street.* *He knows the hole is there and pretends not to see the hole*.......... | On the third day of using the man deliberately avoids any thoughts of the negative impact of his using i.e. on his economic life and his family because these memories affects the high he wants from his drug. |

|  | | |
|---|---|---|
| **Day 4** | *On the fourth day... the man walks cautiously down the street.* *He sees the hole and this time walks around it. He is pleased.* *But the world goes dark again. He has fallen into another hole...............* | On the fourth day the man sits in his house and says he is not going to use crack today. He is more cautious. *However, for whatever reason he has an argument with his wife and he says to her and himself 'fuck it!' and 'fuck you!'. Then he leaves his home and uses crack!* |
| **Day 5** | *On the fifth day... the man walks confidently down the street.* *He sees the first hole............* | On the fifth day the man feels more aware, he stays home which feels, good. But he has another argument with his wife, leaves home and uses, but this time he does not stay there all night. He stays for two hours and for whatever reason he returns home, to the surprise of his wife! |
| **Day 6** | *On the sixth day... the man walks nervously down the street...The hole is there* | The sixth day the man is very aware of his using habits. He knows where the dealer is, and |

| | | |
|---|---|---|
| | *and he thinks "I won't fall into the hole again"... and walks around the hole. He sees the second hole, avoids the second hole... but as he passes, he loses his balance... and falls in. Climbing out he walks back home ... taking the time to carefully avoid all the holes. On the seventh day... the same man goes for a walk....* | he knows his triggers. He even monitors his response to his wife, so he does not argue. He decides to go for a walk, quite happy with himself. On the street he meets a friend, who asks him 'how's things'? He replies 'I'm fine.' The man on the street looks at him and makes a gesture to use. The man looks at him his hands sweaty, his mouth a little dry, and says to himself, 'I've been good, fuck it!' A little smoke will be OK! it's a treat!' The man uses! |
| **Day 7** | **... and chooses to walk down a different street**. | On the seventh day the man is sitting in the living room, by himself..........thinking! |

Let us say that the **hole** represents an obstacle, the second **hole** represents the same obstacle, and more explicitly the **hole** represents crack cocaine, the family, treatment, work etc.

- Is motivation the correct terminology to use when referring to the service user's **desire** to achieve his or her goal around substances?

- Is it worth considering?
- What encourages an individual or group of individuals to re-evaluate what they do and why they do it?
- What if motivation is used over simplistically when exploring with the service user their desire to change?
- Maybe our beliefs in the service user being 'motivated' fundamentally colours how we construct the drugs professional and develop the service.

### Conflicts in Motivation

When we consider motivation in relation to interventions for drug users we often focus on the service user and their motivation to achieve their goals regarding their drug use. Often what we do not look at or explore is the professional's motivation and the motivation of the service. If we do not fully comprehend motivation and what it is in each context, then we may lose sight of why service users, at times, do not achieve their goals.

| Service Users Motivation | Professionals Motivation | The Services Motivation |
|---|---|---|
| Secondary Goal | External Motivation | Coercion: |
| *Crack cocaine: This indirect motivator, or the secondary goal, can become very* | *The professional wants to be 'liked' by the service user. This is the result of an* | *Coercion is to get someone or something to behave in a particular way through* |

| | | |
|---|---|---|
| powerful, and may even eclipse the primary survival/ procreative type motivation. Example: The feelings and euphoria from crack cocaine use become so important that they disrupt the service user's relationship with his/her family leading to his/her children going into care. | **external force** i.e. positive feedback from the service user i.e. 'you are a great worker' which stimulates a particular type of relationship with the service user. | the use of an external force! The hoped for outcome is that the individual will give you something! That 'something' could be obedience, a changed mind set, acknowledgement of the problems they are causing within the community etc. |

*This example shows 3 types of motivation that may well be at odds with one another:*

- The crack cocaine user does not prioritise his/her feelings about their family etc. The drug is the primary force in his/her life.
- The professional operates from a 'people pleasing' position, whose motivation is the recognition from the service user that s/he is a good and caring person.
- The service is one based on the principle of coercion, whereby if the service user follows the rules of the intervention (that have been laid down by the unconscious motivation of the professional) then s/he will be positively rewarded.

In such a situation it is impossible for the intervention to have the best possible impact on the service user because the motivational forces in operation, in this case on the 3 players in this drama, are all 'pulling in different directions'.

The service user, the professional and the service represent three types of motivational drivers coming together and colliding with each other. If the professional, the team, the culture of the service, the theorist, etc. do not take this into account, the effectiveness of the given interventions may be greatly reduced.

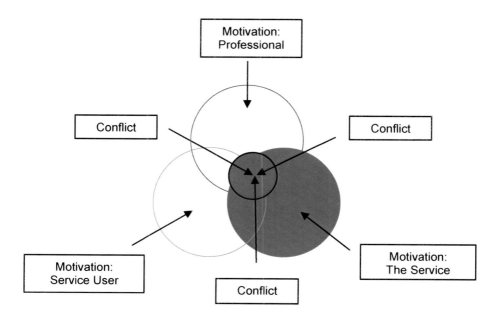

Motivation cannot simply refer to the service user. It must also encompass the professional, and the nature and culture of the service. A suggestion might be to explore the motivations of each of the three groups and then adjust the interventions and expectations accordingly. This requires that the workforce is prepared to examine and re-examine its inherent beliefs around motivation that might lead to an alternative outcome to:

*'This service user needs CBT!'*

If the **mechanism** that informs the worker or the team is simply:

*'CBT is the most effective response to 'crack cocaine' use.'*

Then the service may well not achieve the desired outcomes.

## Motivation and the Service User

Even though the above could well be at the heart of designing interventions which tap more thoughtfully into motivation, we should explore in a little more detail the service user and their relationship with motivation.

## Cognitive Resonance

There is a man who feels happy with himself and his life. He has a partner and even though they talk about children and maybe having children at some time in the future, it is an infrequent topic of conversation. He spends his time at work, going to pubs and wine bars, going to the cinema, having sex and all the other liberties that not having children represents to many.

One day he receives a phone call, and his partner says she would like to meet him after work. He asks her: *'What's the matter?'* and she replies: *'Nothing, I just want to talk to you.'* In his mind he is thinking: *'What have I done wrong?'* but he quickly relaxes and gets back into the routine of his day job.

When they meet up after work, she smiles at him looking happy, yet a little pensive. He says: *'What's the matter?'* and she nods her head saying: *'Nothing. Do you want a drink?' 'Yes'* he replies. *'Well get it then!'* she says and smiles. He returns with the drinks, placing them on the table, sit down she says: *'I'm pregnant.'* He looks at her with surprise.

The following day when he is on his way to work he is shocked by the number of pregnant women he sees; he notices baby shops selling baby shoes, bibs, baby grows etc. When he returns home every other advertisement on telly appears to be promoting baby food and baby shampoo. He cannot believe how much baby stuff there is around him!

## Consider:

- Were the pregnant women, the baby food advertisements etc, not present before?
- What triggered his awareness of babies and pregnant women?
- Why did he not notice them before?

- What is a way of describing this process?

**Perhaps:**

- Pregnant women and baby advertisements were present before he got the news that he was to become a father.
- He only became aware of them after the news from his partner. He became open to the world of fatherhood, because the information from his partner placed the idea of woman, child, man, pregnancy, at the forefront of his mind. He became conscious!
- He did not notice such things before, because he had no reason to recognise them, because they were not relevant to his universe!
- This process could be called **'Cognitive Resonance'**. i.e. we become aware of particular things, babies, for example, when they are attached to something 'core' i.e. being made aware that you are a **father!**
- Resonance will have a number of effects on someone, in this case being made aware of fatherhood. The potential father may:

    - Embrace the idea of fatherhood
    - Run a mile from the prospect of fatherhood
    - Pretend it is not happening
    - Blame the other person

Therefore resonance is an emotional and experience based reality, and how someone manages that new unavoidable reality is important.

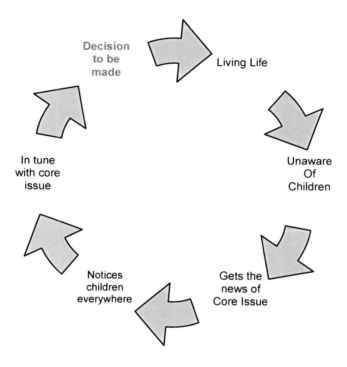

**Resonance, the Obstacle and Motivation**

Should it be a goal of a drugs professional to help the service user identify core things that resonate within them in order to elicit a response from the service user that makes them pause before they use crack or their drug of choice? This can be done in conjunction with 'associations', which are the things the crack cocaine service user comes into contact with through their drug use.

As illustrated, people respond to Resonance in different ways. When informed that you are a father, you may:

- Embrace it

**Or**

- Run a mile

There is therefore a skill implicit in working with Resonance, and perhaps Resonance is one of the pillars that 'motivation' should be built upon.

**Crack Cocaine and Resonance**

An excellent example of resonance with the crack cocaine user is the **toilet flushing syndrome.** As professionals we should not let our 'sensibilities' get in the way of making the service user aware of themselves and the physical environment they exist within in order to create a resonance within themselves when they come up against a 'core' anchor surrounding their use of drugs. This core anchor does not have to be dramatic, for instance a family crisis, or childhood abuse. The **toilet flushing syndrome** is a good example of this!

Adrenaline + Dopamine + Serotonin = **The Toilet Flushing Syndrome**

**Adrenaline** is a powerful hormone whose function is to enhance the physical performance of a person in times of crisis. A common

76

definition is that it is a substance released by the body that prepares the human organism for the response of:

- Fight or
- Flight

That is to say it prepares us to confront a situation or to flee/run away from the situation. With this process comes a particular sensation, which is described as 'butterflies'. 'Butterflies' can be a distinctly uncomfortable sensation that is generated by much of the blood being diverted from the digestive system. This is because the body is preparing for a stressful situation i.e. meeting a girl or boy you are attracted to for the first time; walking through an environment that you fear; having to deal with conflict; going for an interview or preparing to use crack cocaine. You may experience sweating, agitation and great anxiety in anticipation of this event.

Ask an athlete if they empty their bowels before a race! Similarly the crack cocaine user may well visit the toilet in preparation for using.

**Dopamine** is a neuro-transmitter that gives an individual a sense of pleasure. In the case of the crack cocaine user, the dopamine floods the brain giving a massive high, which in most cases outstrips any other pleasurable sensation the crack user will naturally experience.

**Serotonin** is another pleasure related neuro-transmitter. However, through the use of crack cocaine, the action of serotonin changes from being a neuro-transmitter that activates pleasure, to becoming a blocker that **prevents** dopamine from being re-absorbed into the system. As a result of this relationship between dopamine and serotonin, the crack cocaine user cannot get the same level of 'high' or 'buzz' at the beginning of <u>each</u> binge because the release of dopamine is reduced each time the crack user uses. This is why we often hear:

## The first use of 'a binge' is the best!

Using the toilet tank as an analogy, the water in the cistern represents dopamine. If you use the toilet and then flush the cistern, the system works perfectly. However:

- What would happen if you were to flush the toilet again immediately after the first time?
  - The toilet would not flush because the cistern is still empty.

This is very much the same way that dopamine works. Because the dopamine has not had enough time to replenish itself within the brain after being stimulated by cocaine use, less and less of it can be released and the anticipated 'high' after the initial binge use of crack use becomes commensurately less.

### Creating Cognitive Resonance in the Crack Cocaine Service User

A reason for awareness training around the effects of crack cocaine on the body i.e. how it affects adrenaline, dopamine and serotonin is to create resonance in the service user. The toilet tank in this case becomes a key imagery tool for the service user.

**The process**

| Service User presents at a service: | The drugs professionals response: |
| --- | --- |
| The service user presents at a service with very little knowledge about crack cocaine and is unclear as to why they feel the way they feel. The service user mentions:<br><br>▪ The high<br>▪ The crash<br>▪ Paranoia<br>▪ Anxiety etc.<br><br><br><br>Remember, the service user is unaware! | The professional focuses on the effects of adrenaline. The worker informs the service user that with the release of adrenalin s/he may experience:<br><br>Agitation<br>Paranoia<br>Moody behaviour<br>Sweating<br>Butterflies etc.<br><br>The professional informs the crack cocaine user that these are some of the body's responses to crack cocaine |
| The service user states that s/he was not aware of the information the professional has given him/her. | The professional responds by talking about why the crack cocaine user experiences butterflies, and then connects the experience of butterflies to going to the toilet before a binge. The |

| | professional explains this to the service user, who acknowledges that they act out this behaviour before using. |
|---|---|
| The service user now has awareness, both:<br>• of the effects of adrenaline and<br>• using behaviour i.e. going to the toilet before using crack. | The drugs professional then takes time to explain the effects of dopamine i.e. dopamine floods the system when someone uses crack cocaine and that is what gives that 'incredible' high. |
| The service user acknowledges his/her new awareness around why s/he gets that incredible high. Then the service user talks about the 'comedown', the 'crash'. | The drugs professional uses the analogy of the toilet flushing system i.e. the high of the dopamine release is very much like the flush of the toilet. However the problem arises when you use crack cocaine immediately again. The result is a 'high' that is not as incredible as at the beginning of the binge. The professional asks the question: What happens if you flush the toilet immediately after the first flush? The crack cocaine user replies: *It won't flush because there isn't enough water in the tank.* |

| The crack cocaine user realises that the initial release of dopamine gives him/her a fantastic 'buzz' however like the flush of the water tank, the 'buzz' will be reduced or made negligible through prolonged use. This informs the crack cocaine user that:<br><br>■ The buzz of the drug cannot be sustained<br>■ The depletion of dopamine is the cause of the 'crash' that the crack cocaine user experiences | The drugs professional has:<br><br>■ Educated the service user about the effects of crack cocaine on the body<br>■ Identified an 'association' (the toilet flush) for the service user<br>■ Created a 'core issue' (resonance) for the service user |
|---|---|
| **The crack cocaine user is in a state of cognitive resonance, much like the man when he first learned he was going to be a father!** | |

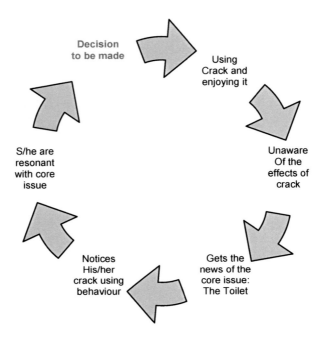

Decision to be made

Using Crack and enjoying it

Unaware Of the effects of crack

S/he are resonant with core issue

Notices His/her crack using behaviour

Gets the news of the core issue: The Toilet

What the crack cocaine user does with this new resonance is up to them, however they can no longer avoid their awareness of their crack use. The obstacle, crack cocaine, and the association with 'the toilet flush' is a functional reminder and continues to resonate with them, every time they use it.

# *Chapter Five*

## Cravings

Crack cocaine has often been described as highly 'addictive'. A crack cocaine user might present to a service saying: 'I hate crack, I want to stop using'. They often say that the impact of the drug is destroying their lives, and in essence they cannot afford to use the drug any more because they fear going to jail, losing their family or going insane.

In reality crack cocaine is no more addictive than tobacco or alcohol. The impact of the drug on health is no greater than those drugs either. On the cigarette pack, one can find the statement:

**Cigarettes Kill!**

Yet people still smoke and in many cases to a degree that it impairs their health or kills them. So why do people continue to use a substance when they are fully aware of the potential damage it can cause?

**Because they like it!**

We can say that the crack user uses a drug:

- To escape
- For confidence
- To socialise
- For creativity
- Because of peer pressure
- Because of boredom

Let us investigate these statements:

| Service User says 'I use': | | Drugs Professional responds: | |
|---|---|---|---|
| To escape | √ | Escape from what?  And for how long?  Do you come back to more chaos than you sought to escape? | X |
| For confidence | √ | Does crack cocaine ever make you feel paranoid? | X |
| To socialise | √ | With whom and in what way? | X |
| For creativity | √ | How long can you maintain your concentration? | X |
| Because of peer pressure | √ | Does that mean you would do everything your peers told you to? | X |
| Because of boredom | √ | What does boredom mean to you? | X |

The most obvious reason to use is because the user loves the 'high' and the buzz associated with acquisition and preparation.

The reasons outlined in this table, all feed into the 'buzz'.  They give the user a multitude of justifications to continue using.  How often do professionals investigate these justifications or alternatively, simply adjust them to their own perspective and then agree?

Exploration of the service user's justifications is crucial as this forms the foundation for exploring cravings and triggers.

We can view cravings and triggers as a multi-disciplinary team; in other words, one does what the other cannot. The role of the trigger is to trigger the thought which may occur when the service user meets a person they have previously used with or when they see a coke can etc. The role of the craving is similar to that of a salesperson. Their remit is to sell the thought of using as an attractive proposition to the individual. The joint purpose of cravings and triggers is to disassociate the person from their conscious knowledge of the detrimental effects of their drug use, because guilt will simply get in the way of the buzz. For example, a craving will not allow the user to remember that they will not eat for the rest of the week if today all their money is spent on crack.

## **Blatant and Silent Cravings**

Service users often spend a lot of time showing workers their lack of awareness. They might say:

- I didn't know
- I didn't see
- If only I knew that
- It happened before I could do anything about it
- S/he put it in my face. What could I do about it?

- I shouldn't have gone there
- I was bored
- Bill came to see me, I didn't know he had drugs on him
- If I had known I wouldn't have let him in
- I was lonely
- I was angry
- I felt like 'shit'!
- I didn't think one stone would hurt
- The cat came through the catflap!

Apart from the cat coming through the flap, we have probably heard many of the above reasons from service users. Their relationship with cravings is often the foundation of their drug use and it is arguable that one can ever use without first experiencing a craving. By drawing a client's attention to this, the process of education begins. For example, a worker may ask the client who says s/he can use without craving: 'How are you when the dealer is 5 minutes late?' When the client describes their impatience, the worker can then help them to understand how that behaviour is based on their craving, or in other words their desire to use. If they had no craving, why would they have any response to the dealer's lateness?

**The Blatant Craving**

The blatant craving is the one that the service user is likely to have a full understanding of. It talks to them in a language that they fully understand. For example: 'It's Friday, I just got paid, I know what I'm doing tonight!' This is clear and non-negotiable for at this point in time the client will not allow anything to get in the way. (The professional's job is to **get in the way!**  This can be done by re-engaging the client with their conscious awareness in any area of their drug use, eg. the comedown, what their partner will say, paying the rent etc.)  The service user may explain this type of craving by saying 'I'm on a mission'.  This means:

- they are on a straight path
- they have a sense of purpose
- their path becomes a tunnel
- they are focused on one thing only
- the anticipation is wondrous!
- they are happy if everything is going according to plan
- they are frustrated if anything is getting in the way of the drug
- there are absolutely no illusions as to where they are going and what they are going to do next

This craving speaks a very clear language that the service user and those around them understand very well.

**The Silent Craving**

The silent craving is said to speak in a foreign language that the service user says s/he does not understand.  This craving usually materialises when a service user makes a decision to either reduce or stop their using.  A craving is, as identified previously, a salesperson, and as such, is not accustomed to being engaged in battle.  The craving now realises that it has to be more devious and change the way it communicates with its subject.  This could be seen as the craving putting on a disguise.  The silent craving takes a service user on a journey but does not disclose the destination until it transforms itself into a blatant craving. The role of the professional is to expose the silent craving with the service user. One way to do this is by using the 'blind window' identified in chapter 2.

**Paul's story:**

- Paul has not used crack for 3 months
- He feels happy and strong that day
- He is getting on much better with his partner
- It's Saturday and he has decided to go to a football match with his friends
- He hasn't been in 3 months, and this is a wonderful treat!
- He meets his friends at his local pub
- He decides to have a drink to get into the spirit of things
- He goes into the stadium, his 'blood' is up, his team wins
- He is hugging and kissing people
- His friend asks him if he wants to go for a drink after the match
- He calls his partner and says he's just going for a quick drink
- His partner is not happy and says: *'Just come home, you've had a good time!'*
- He says: *'Don't worry, I'll just have one drink then I will come straight home.'*
- Paul comes home the following morning after a cocaine binge!

The above scenario is not uncommon and exemplifies the work of a silent craving. Because the silent craving does not inform the individual of its agenda, i.e. Paul did not go out planning to use, it did not appear to be necessary to put a plan in place to negate the potential dangers. Alternatively, being 3 months drug free, Paul should have had some understanding of his silent cravings. He might just have been serving his own interests and choosing to ignore the triggers, eg. drinking and football match, that would have alerted him to the probable existence of a silent craving. Also it is important to acknowledge that as an avid supporter going to a football match, Paul would most likely experience the euphoria caused by the release of dopamine and adrenaline in his system. Paul might easily associate this feeling with his previous crack cocaine use as the same chemicals are activated.

In helping Paul to examine what happened, a worker might ask:

- Why was he happy?
- Why did he decide to go to the football match?
- Why did he go to the pub and have a drink first?
- Why did he return to the pub after the match?
- Why did he not hear the concern in his partner's voice?
- When did he say to himself?: *'Fuck it!'*

If Paul is able to honestly answer these questions and thereby expose the silent craving, he can then use this process for internal dialogue in a future situation **while it is actually happening.**

**What to do with cravings?**

Cravings are a part of the natural human condition. If we were dying of thirst and did not crave water we would die. Professionals often steer the service user away from their cravings by encouraging them to do something to take their mind away from their desire to use drugs. A more effective way to manage cravings is to acknowledge them and enter into a **dialogue** with them. The service user needs to become aware of the difference between the blatant craving and the silent craving. S/he then needs to learn how to speak the language of the silent craving and not be duped by it. By creating an inner dialogue with their cravings, the service user is developing self-awareness. What is promoted here is a way that the service user can actually communicate with themselves. By diverting service users from their cravings, we are actually diverting them away from themselves thus decreasing their capacity for self-awareness.

Cravings represent an overt or covert desire to use drugs. If we were to find that the desire to use is for pleasure, then that is where the work begins.

When the service user really wants to reduce or stop their drug use, they need to be made aware that they are entering a battlefield. The service user needs to know that a craving knows all of their vulnerabilities because it is a part of them. Therefore to create a level playing field, the user needs to know all about the craving. The worker needs to make the user aware that before they enter the battle zone, they need to research the enemy so that they know what armour is the most appropriate to avoid getting wounded. A human being is adept at playing games with him/herself, and will deceive themselves for a variety of reasons. One of the most important things for the service user to know is that a craving will pass with time, unless s/he has already made a conscious decision to use.

**How to get to know a craving**

A man and his partner have just split up after 5 years together. He goes to a restaurant where they used to eat. He gets 'euphoric recall' remembering all the good times they had together. At no time does he think about the bad times. As he is leaving the restaurant it so happens that his ex-partner is entering the restaurant with a friend. He gets butterflies in his stomach but does not understand why. He asks her how she is. She says: 'Not bad, but could you come and see me later, I want to talk'? All the way to her house, he is assuring himself that it is only to talk. She answers the door in her negligee, and he remembers the good sexual relationship they had. They end up spending the night together. In the morning he asks himself: 'How did I get here?'

This scenario is one that many of us can relate to. It does not particularly relate to drug users, but it illustrates triggers (the restaurant) and cravings (butterflies) and denial (only to talk). The questions he could have asked himself:

- Why am I going to **this** restaurant?
- What were the real reasons we split up?
- Why am I going to her house?
- What is there to talk about?

91

- Why is she wearing this negligee?!

These questions are honest and factual and therefore demand honest and factual answers. The aim of these questions is to expose how this man was deceiving himself from the outset, i.e., from the moment he set foot in the restaurant.

The way a crack user may go though this process, particularly someone who has had a period of abstinence can be as follows:

- I'm going to visit my old using friend, but I'm not going to use
- I'm just going to have one stone
- I won't have a pipe, I'll smoke it in a joint

Questions for the service user to ask him/herself:

- Why take the risk of being in the company of an old using friend?
- When have I ever had just one stone?
- Will smoking it in a joint make me crave it any less?

Over a period of time this self-questioning will become part of the service user's armoury to address their cravings both blatant and silent. This equips them with skills and information about themselves that will enable them to make informed decisions. The process of self-questioning can change a silent craving to a blatant craving which the user is then fully aware of. If at this point the decision to use is affirmed, then it is by conscious choice and is usually accompanied by the:

**'Fuck It Syndrome!'**
**(Please excuse the language)**

# Chapter Six

## Reasons and Justifications

*Who is the best psychologist, the worker or the client?*

**Justifications and Excuses within Key working, Counselling and Group Work.**

When a professional comes into contact with a service user, they may seem to enter an unusual house where the service user is represented by 2 tenants. The first tenant is Mr or Mrs 'Reason' the other is Mr or Mrs 'Justification'. These tenants exceed the usual interpretations of:

Mr or Mrs 'Reason' = Legitimate
Mr or Mrs 'Justification' = Excuse

Mr or Mrs **'Reason'** says:

- The come down is unbearable!
  - *That's why I use!*
    - *And I the professional believe you!*

- I have so much emotional pain!
  - *That's why I use!*

- *And I the professional believe you!*

- You don't know what a crack 'crash' is like
  - *That's why I use!*
    - *And I the professional believe you!*

- I cannot cope!
  - *That's why I use!*
    - *And I the professional believe you!*

- I am depressed!
  - *That's why I use!*
    - *And I the professional believe you!*

This list goes on. When the professional hears these reasons they can feel powerless in the face of such powerful 'reasons' to use crack cocaine.

Using the same examples Mr or Mrs **'Justification'** says:

- The come down is unbearable!
  - *That's why I use!*
    - *And I the professional **do not** believe you!*

- I have so much emotional pain!
  - *That's why I use!*
    - *And I the professional **do not** believe you!*

- You don't know what a crack 'crash' is like!
  - *That's why I use!*

- *And I the professional **do not** believe you!*

- I cannot cope!
    - *That's why I use!*
        - *And I the professional **do not** believe you!*

- I am depressed!
    - *That's why I use!*
        - *And I the professional **do not** believe you!*

In this case the professional views the service users 'reasons' as 'excuses'. Internally the professional will make presumptive leaps, based on their own training, life experience etc, to reach a decision as to whether the service user has a 'legitimate reason' or is 'making excuses' in order to continue using crack/cocaine.

The professional is often faced with 'reasons' and 'justifications' from a service user and this can lead to a crossroads. Which direction should the professional take? This decision is not only influenced by 'objectivity' and 'professional training'. The professional may need to investigate the client's statements. Also **the professional may need to ask themselves:**

*Is it possible to use a drug over a long period of time, in a chaotic or problematic way, without either justifying the action, or making an excuse?*

The answer to this question will influence our response to the client and may consequently inhibit their progress, their self-awareness and their capacity to make informed choices. In some cases this may lead to collusion with the client that allows them to remain at the same level of drug use and associated chaos.

In this case the workers interventions may be based on the following:

- **Supposition**: when someone believes something to be true without any proof
- **Assumption**: something that you accept as true without question or proof
- **Presumption**: when you believe something is true without having any proof

These can influence direct interventions such as:

- Did you use drugs yesterday?
  - Yes or No!
    - The professional then either believes or disbelieves.

Or beliefs about the client such as:

- S/he is aggressive or
- S/he is unable to change

It would be interesting to explore how much of our viewpoint regarding justifications and reasons are simply hereditary i.e. passed down historically from one generation of workers to another or from one generation of clients to another! It is important therefore to ask questions in all aspects of our work, and with each individual client, rather than assume, suppose or presume.

Our view of the distinction between a justification and a reason shapes our view of a service user's relationship with 'dependency'. Therefore our attitude towards dependency will very much dictate whether the professional **supports** the service user or **colludes** with the service user.

**Let us explore!**

*As a professional ask yourself this question!*

*Is boredom a trigger to use a drug?*
*Yes or No! (And please do not sit on the fence!)*

We can find 'boredom' written into care plans, discussed in 1 to 1 sessions, manifesting itself in therapeutic groups, drug intervention groups and so on. Boredom has been identified as a major trigger for drug use and is often a core theme in planning relapse prevention and lapse management.

*Case Study*

*John has been 'relapsing' for months. He says that his trigger is 'boredom'! He states that whenever he leaves the project, the feeling of being bored and having nothing to do kicks in.*

The professionals working with John actively worked with his boredom, building it into his care plan, identifying activities that John had said that he has enjoyed in the past, and which he feels he could do now. No matter the intervention being used, his boredom was acknowledged and worked with by the whole team. The core theme of the work around him was to:

*Enable John to fill his time with activities!*

For a variety of reasons professionals respond to the idea of boredom in similar ways, i.e. *to find something for the service user to do.* This represents an established belief passed on from one professional to another that has been learned through training or experience and says that **'boredom is a legitimate reason for using drugs'.** Therefore the way we respond to boredom is '**historic'** and our interventions are *automatic* and executed without debate.

The objective of the drugs professional should be:

*To listen out for what the client is not saying!*

*Is part of the role of the drug user to deflect the drugs professional away from their real agenda i.e. to use drugs?*

How could we encourage and allow John to explore and challenge his thought processes around whether or not boredom is either a 'reason' or a 'justification'? Therefore, is 'boredom' a genuine trigger to use crack or is it an excuse?

100

### John's unexpected session!

One day, by chance, John saw a different worker. John fell into his normal pattern of identifying boredom as a key reason/trigger for his using. He also stated that he felt unable to do the activities identified in his care plan. As he began to explain himself, the new worker asked him what appeared to be a very obvious question:

### What does boredom mean to you?

John became confused and angry by this question. However through exploration John eventually replied:

### Having nothing to do!

When the worker asked John what he had to do in his home, he said he had a:

- Television
- DVD
- Computer

He further stated that these things 'bored' him.

*What did the new worker do? The new worker separated:*

- Having nothing to do!'

*from*

- 'I was bored!'

*In a single session he explored the fact that 'having nothing to do' and 'being bored' were quite separate issues.*

*The worker then asked John how much money he had spent on crack cocaine the night before.*

*John responded that he had spent £400.00 during the previous day.*

*The worker asked John if he enjoyed holidays in the sun. John replied 'yes'.*

*The worker responded that John could have flown to the Caribbean for this amount of money in order to alleviate his 'boredom'!*

Both John and the drug service had become complacent regarding his 'boredom'. The service legitimised the reason behind John's drug use, by giving him permission to use whenever he felt 'bored', because they carried on identifying *new activities!* What John was actually saying was that for him everything, apart from smoking crack cocaine, was boring. This allowed John to focus on the issue of 'boredom' rather than his 'cravings' that precipitated his using.

*It is probably fair to reflect that the service probably responded to many service users in the same way around the issue of 'boredom'.*

## An exploration of the process

| | The Process |
|---|---|
| 1 | John's justification that 'boredom' was a legitimate trigger, was validated both by his peers and more importantly by his drugs worker. (Remember, clients usually carry the assumption that the key worker is always right!). |
| 2 | His key worker did not take on board that dependency is a very complex issue and can be very devious especially when someone's desire to use becomes great. Also, the role of the professional is to get in the way of a service user's drug use. Because his keyworker was not getting in the way of his using, John was able, consciously or unconsciously, to continue to throw the obstacle of boredom at the drugs worker. |
| 3 | John's key worker, like many professionals, no matter their background, experience and training, responded to this descriptive term 'boredom' from his own viewpoint of what boredom meant to him personally. This is often problematic for the service user. Boredom is often viewed, as a legitimate 'trigger' to use. |
| 4 | By focusing on the word boredom, it was hard for John to realise that the real issue was his *craving*. Is it possible to use without first getting a craving? However because it had been agreed, by the service user, the professional, and the service, that boredom was the trigger, there was no stimulus for John to think about the *craving*. <br><br> If symbolically John had put his desire to use in a **box,** a box called boredom, had the service merely **colluded** with him, allowing him to use his drug of choice with its blessing? |

| | |
|---|---|
| 5 | In certain situations, we can often feel a block when it comes to challenging clients, as we may feel that challenging = conflict. Does our difficulty with conflict at times allow us to be 'held hostage'? Our role as practitioners is to support a client in **investigating** their own statements, in order for them to learn to use new tools when required. |
| 6 | Taking drugs was very pleasurable and John felt everything else was boring. His brain was telling him that **all** the pleasure he gets in his life, is from crack cocaine. This emotional dynamic was only intensifying John's cravings to use. The role of the drugs professional was to bring this awareness to the forefront of his mind, thereby taking him to a place where he could make informed choices. |
| 7 | As human beings there will always be times when we feel 'bored'. *But what exactly does boredom mean to you?* |

**Reasons and Justifications**

Is it possible for an individual to use crack cocaine or any drug without a 'justification'? As soon as we say that the individual has a 'legitimate reason' to use or to act out their behaviour around their drug of choice, are we at that moment 'drugs workers' or are we 'colluding', especially if a drugs worker's role is to encourage the service user to explore their motives for using drugs in greater depth?

A common justification for someone using a drug is 'poor self esteem' or in other words they may be saying, 'you are better than me because I use crack!' The drugs professional often colludes with this stance, legitimising this particular form of 'justification'. **However this is not a legitimate reason!**

Justification is at the heart of drug use! However, this is not an issue for the drug user, but it **is** a major issue for the professional and the culture of the service. With crack cocaine we often say:

- Crack is the most addictive of all drugs.
  - Is that true?
    - No!

- Crack and mental health go hand in hand!
  - Is that true?
    - No!

- The crash, the come down from crack is too much! It's horrendous!
  - Is that true? It is bad but is it unmanageable?
    - No!

One could argue that there are service users to whom the above statements are applicable. We would argue that this has led to some damaging responses to, and interventions for the crack cocaine user. Let us not react to just one or two isolated cases, but respond proactively to this whole service user group.

The drugs professional is the key to how the service user views his/her own drug use. The language, the ethos and the culture that a team develops around 'justifications and reasons' for drug use can,

105

with clarification and co-operation, improve the qualitative care and outcomes for this service user group, and in truth for drug users across the board.

**And remember:** 'boredom' as an example, is not a reason to use a drug! Perhaps if all professionals were to ask: 'What does boredom mean to you?' this would remove a major trigger from the clients armoury.

# *Chapter Seven*

## Trust

*I Inform Myself!*

In order to assess one's own performance, a worker can use the exercise below. In particular the exercise can evaluate:

- how well they perform
- how aware they are
- how able they are to relate to a given issue

If we ask ourselves a question, through an awareness exercise, we can examine what happens using a 4 stage process.

### Stage 1

From a scale of 1 to 10 (1 being the lowest – 10 being the highest) how well do you think you work with and engage the crack cocaine service user?

Then ask yourself how you reached the score you gave yourself. Was it:

- I am a good listener

- I am a good communicator
- I am empathetic
- I've used drugs myself in the past, I know where s/he is coming from
- I am a trained therapist/psychologist/nurse/psychiatrist.....
- My gut feeling tells me
- I live in a diverse environment
- I base my work on 'evidence based practice'

As you read the above place a tick by the ones that apply to you. Feel free to add more to the list.

*Take some time to reflect before the next stage.*

## Stage 2

*How did you achieve the score you gave yourself?  Was it through:*

- honest feedback from the client group?
- the effective use of supervision?
- colleague feedback?
- a well informed induction review when you began working at your current service?
- an end of year appraisal?
- your service hitting challenging targets to engage crack cocaine service users?

## Stage 3

Now consider whether you:

- were informed through your **internal self-evaluation** (stage 1) or by **external forces** (stage 2)?

**Stage 4**

Now ask yourself what might be gained or lost when an individual, or service, uses only their own tools to measure or evaluate their own performance. Furthermore, consider what might be gained, or lost, when an individual, or service, uses tools external to themselves, eg. feedback from clients, colleagues, to measure their skills and ability.

Janus Solutions believes that professionals no matter their standing should not be allowed to only inform themselves as to their effectiveness with regards to working with crack cocaine users.

This exercise relates equally to a service, a management team, an organisation and to those involved in policy and strategy development. It is important to realise that no individual drugs professional, no matter their skill base, is excluded from this process of evaluation.

**How do we create:**

- Individual professional awareness
- Service awareness
- Organisational awareness?

We can do this through encouraging openness and engaging in **hot communication**, i.e. communication that focuses on 'taboo' themes. When we aim to engage and treat crack cocaine users, we can either view this negatively because of the 'enigma' that is crack cocaine, or we can view it as a learning opportunity that might better prepare us for the next 'enigma' that we might face eg. meth-amphetamine. Perhaps also there are lessons that we can learn from our experience with crack cocaine that could well inform our work with users of opiates, alcohol, benzo-diazepines etc. Bearing in mind that crack cocaine has been around for over two decades, we have to ask ourselves:

***What went wrong?  What did we do wrong?***

Perhaps it is also a good time to ask if current substance use service provision across the board is stuck in an historical quagmire that will ultimately create problems for future treatment and intervention.

**A way forward for the professional and the service!**

Regarding the crack cocaine service user, professionals and services even though 'well intentioned', may have created many problems for themselves. Has the approach used for this service user group been reactionary and anxiety led or has it been wrapped in mythological beliefs such as:

| |
|---|
| Crack cocaine is probably more associated with mental health than any other drug. |
| Most crack cocaine users have first contact with substance misuse services through the criminal justice system. |
| The language of neurology is often used by professionals working with the crack cocaine user.  What happens after the dopamine-seratonin-adrenalin explanation is given, that is if the worker actually |

understands it themselves!

*Note:* *If the explanation of how neurotransmitters work is so relevant to the crack cocaine service user, why is this knowledge not generally part of our tool bag for our work with other drug users?*

As mentioned previously, crack cocaine is not a new drug. It has been prevalent for more than twenty years and its use and impact on individuals, communities and services is huge. We are firm advocates of 'Emotional Intelligence' for working with this service user group. This concept is not new, and can be applied in all aspects of one's life, the professional context being only one.

Emotional Intelligence is an excellent tool that challenges us in assessing 'how good and how competent' we are when:

- engaging the service user,
- working within a team
- constructing a service.

Whether you are a Psychiatrist, Drugs Worker, Nurse, Probation Officer, Receptionist etc., you require emotional intelligence to be effective in what you do. We are not immune to being judgemental and discriminatory in our work practice, and the crack cocaine user has been experiencing this from us for too long. If we accept this to be true, how many crack cocaine users have therefore been detrimentally affected by the working practice of professionals?

**Let us make a few bold statements:**

**Statement 1**

- There is no definitive expertise in the field of substance use neither in psychiatry, psychotherapy nor in those who study addictive behaviour.

- Of course there are individuals with helpful, relevant and highly developed skills, however there are no definitive **experts!**

*Are these statements rash or ill considered, or are they a demonstration of strong* **'Emotional Intelligence'?**

**Statement 2**

- Services do not fulfil their true partnership potential because of the benefits enjoyed by maintaining traditional hierarchies, and a fundamental lack of respect between professionals and services.

- Of course many professionals and related services do work well together, but how many professionals feel the above holds true at the same time?

> - *Are these statements rash or ill considered, or are they a demonstration of strong* **'Emotional Intelligence'?**

## Statement 3

> - The crack cocaine user is far more stigmatised than the cocaine powder user.
>
> ---
>
> - Of course the 'high' you get from smoking crack cocaine is more intense that from cocaine powder, but they are still both 'cocaine'!
>
> ---
>
> - *Are these statements rash or ill considered, or are they a demonstration of strong* **'Emotional Intelligence'?**

## What is Emotional Intelligence?

Emotional Intelligence can be explored within different frameworks, and it is easy to approach it from an intellectual place that allows the participants to fool themselves that 'they are Emotionally Intelligent' and therefore 'well balanced'. However, Emotional Intelligence goes beyond the idea that 'I am a very nice person!' to a place where we ask: 'How can I enhance my awareness of myself and my team and

113

develop our service accordingly? Some professionals and teams fall into the easy trap of believing, or behaving as though they have achieved their maximum potential and have nothing else to learn.

**The Model**

## 5 aspects of Emotional Intelligence

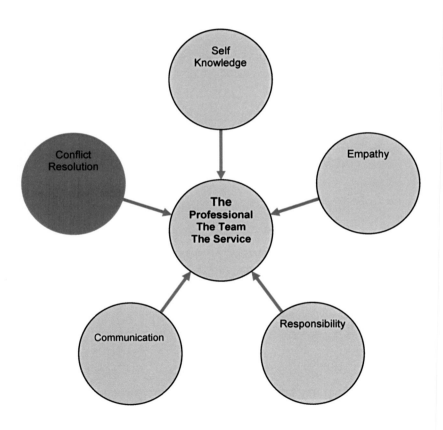

**Self Knowledge constitutes:**

- Knowing what you are feeling
- Knowing how this affects how you behave
- Knowing when your 'self defence' mechanism kicks in

**Empathy constitutes:**

- Appreciating how others feel
- Understanding how others interpret experience differently from you
- Accepting that others' feelings are different from your own

**Responsibility constitutes:**

- Accepting that you, and only you, are responsible for your behaviour
- Understanding that whilst you may not be able to control what you feel, you can control your behaviour
- Everyone (in a team or an organisation) accepting responsibility for the success of the whole project or task, not merely their part of it

**Communication constitutes that:**

- Communication with respect is essential
- Effective communication can only be achieved without put-downs, sarcasm or innuendo
- People communicate in different ways. Assumptions about mood/feelings such as aggression, fear etc. are largely culture specific

**Conflict Resolution constitutes:**

- Conflict resolution in the workplace is mostly about resolving people's feelings
- It is not until people are able to express how they feel that conflict can begin to be resolved
- Conflict resolution is usually only effective when people are calm (not angry, frustrated etc.)

Note: If issues are not resolved in a clear and transparent way then the team and the individual are disrupted.

The above illustrates that the way individuals responds within a team will ultimately dictate the nature of the service. The interesting thing about Emotional Intelligence is that it does not on the surface appear to be applicable to service development. However what Emotional Intelligence recognises is that a team cannot develop and shape the service it delivers if professionals lack the emotional maturity to see the world from a place other than from their own limited perspective. This is something, that afflicts interventions for crack cocaine service users and we must bear in mind that this also applies in the development of policy and strategy. In addition, we may well want to ask: 'how much of evidence based research is shaped by emotional intelligence?'

**How can Emotional Intelligence be applied to the development of a service?**

It is necessary to take ownership of what is currently taking place in the service, followed by a collective responsibility to make positive changes.

**4 stages of Trust:**

| **Predictability:** |
| --- |
| **Definition:** *Trust means being able to predict what other people will do and what situations will occur. If we can surround ourselves with people we trust, then we can create a safe present, and an even better future.* |
| Does the crack cocaine user trust the service, the knowledge of the professionals and the ability to focus on the correct issues? How 'safe' does the service user feel within a service?<br>Note: we are talking about the sense of trust and safety being created by 'attention to detail' when developing crack cocaine provision. |

**Value Exchange**

**Definition:** *Trust means making an exchange with someone when you do not have full knowledge about them, their intent and the things they are offering to you.*

The crack cocaine user presents to a service looking for understanding and effective communicative interventions. They hope for the aforementioned, but they do not know 'YOU!', nor do they know what you will be offering them. They **hope** that the value of the exchange will be of a high quality!

**Delayed Reciprocity**

**Definition:** *Trust means giving something now with an expectation that it will be repaid, possibly in some unspecified way, at some unspecified time, in the future.*

When the crack cocaine user presents, they expect that the professional and service will repay that gesture by providing the appropriate service. It is not uncommon for a crack cocaine user to be misdiagnosed as having a mental health problem. Although some of this user group do have mental health issues, most do not.

118

**Exposed Vulnerabilities**

**Definition:** *Trust means enabling other people to take advantage of your vulnerabilities - but expecting that they will not do this.*

When a crack service user approaches a service they are putting their vulnerability into your hands, and you have to be mindful as to how you hold that vulnerability. It is our responsibility to return it to the appropriate place, reasonably intact.

The above definitions of trust demonstrate an interesting approach that could easily be developed into a framework to inform us about the quality of relationship we are developing with this client group.

# Chapter Eight

## Diversity and Crack Cocaine Use

Diversity is a sticky subject, and one that is often spoken about in whispers. It is relevant to everybody involved in crack cocaine use: the crack cocaine user who is looking to access a service; the service user who is already in a service; the professionals who are providing a service and the fundamental construct of treatment services per se.

*In America in the late 1970s, crack first came on the scene in the form of cocaine freebasing. Many of its users were stockbrokers and investment bankers, rock stars, Hollywood types, and a few professional athletes. Some of them began to get into trouble with this form of cocaine use, showing up in hospital emergency rooms and police stations. Congress passed new laws to extend health insurance coverage to include drug treatment and the treatment industry expanded the number of beds available.*

*In the mid-1980s, crack use spread into America's inner cities among impoverished African Americans and Latinos. This new user group also began to present in hospital emergency rooms and police stations. Congress passed new laws to extend the length of criminal sentences for crack offences and the prison industry expanded the number of cells available.*

*The new laws against crack helped to drive the largest wave of imprisonment in the history of the United States (Bureau of Justice 1995). The number of drug offenders in prison grew eightfold, from about 50,000 in the early Reagan years to about 400,000 at the start of the Bush administration. This bulging prison population was disproportionately comprised of poor people of colour, who had not committed violent crimes (Irwin and Austin, 1994; Parenti, 1991; Bureau of Justice Statistics, 2001).*

*(Crack in the Rearview Mirror: Deconstructing Drug War Mythology: Craig Reinarman and Harry G. Levine, 2002)*

**Diversity and Convenience**

It is important for us as professionals to reflect on our relationship with treatment interventions.  Do we operate outside the spectrum of influence called 'diversity'?  Of course not!

- Strategy
- Policy
- Theory
- Practice

These can all be shaped by diversity!  The excerpt from Reinarman and Levine's work illustrates that how something is viewed, in this case the crack cocaine user, can directly impact whole swathes of the population.  In addition, that perception can influence how a particular drug using group receives treatment and how they are viewed by the wider community.

The drugs professional at times spins a web of justification, which allows them to carry on providing the same old interventions whether they are effective or not. It is this inability of the professional to look deeper into the history and context of crack cocaine, which ultimately limits the scope and flexibility of interventions. We spend time saying:

- Cognitive Behavioural Therapy is the key
- Motivational Interviewing is the key
- Relapse Prevention is the key
- Acupuncture is the key
- Psychotherapy is the key
- That the Criminal Justice System is the environment through which many crack cocaine service users will receive their first treatment intervention.

The list goes on! However Janus believes that the self awareness of the professional is the key. That the ability to truly critically evaluate crack in its widest and in its most holistic context is the key. One cannot look at crack cocaine service users without looking at diversity and one could go as far as to say that the rise in crack cocaine use led to an increased focus on diversity. If we made a case study of crack cocaine, and saw where we went wrong, then much could be learned to enhance our practice with all drug users.

## What is Diversity?

Diversity is a wide-ranging subject and one that we often trivialise. Why? Because of fear? How often do we hear 'I'm not prejudice, I treat everyone the same'? This statement prevents further exploration of this complex subject and the individuals' self-examination of their core beliefs and how they are shaped. Those beliefs are shaped by many personal, social and institutional factors that influence how we see the client who sits in front of us. As services are made up of individuals, so those internalised beliefs therefore influence the culture of the service, the organisation within which the service operates and ultimately the policies that are devised and operated by that organisation.

Diversity also goes far beyond our individual psychology, it relates more to how prepared we are to explore that psychology and ultimately expand it, thus opening the door to a richer engagement with others.

### Cognitive Dissonance

It is important for us to consider why the crack/cocaine user was, and is, at times viewed almost as a demonic character. The partners at Janus Solutions have worked with all types of drug users, including hundreds of crack cocaine users and have very rarely experienced them to be problematic in the stereotypical ways often described, that is:

- Aggressive
- Violent
- Prone to radical mood swings
- Psychotic etc

Cognitive Dissonance is a way of looking at diversity in a way that takes a slightly different route to the normal frameworks and concepts that are used when looking at diversity. We will draw on the work of Dr Joy DeGruy Leary, who focussed on a subject called 'Post Traumatic Slave Syndrome' **(PTSS)** when looking at relationships based on difference. She explored the accepted belief amongst many people in America that 'blacks' were inferior to 'whites'. She identified that Native Americans fell into the same sub-group as those from African Descent. The questions Dr Joy Leary asked were:

- Why did those views come to be widely held?
- Why did the humanity of Africans as well as Native Americans come into question?

She concluded and identified the relationship between cognitive dissonance and diversity as follows:

*When we commit a negative act or think about doing so most of us get uncomfortable. This discomfort is caused by the difference between our action and what we believe about ourselves. For example, most of us would experience a certain amount of discomfort if we were to seriously consider robbing someone and even greater discomfort if we were to actually do it. Why? Because most of us think of ourselves as decent people and decent people do not rob others. This discomfort is called 'Cognitive Dissonance'. Cognitive – having to do with thinking: Dissonance – meaning discord. The greater the difference between our actions and what we think about ourselves, the greater the dissonance and so, our discomfort.*

**She goes on to say:**

*Humans do not particularly like this discomfort so whenever it occurs we almost immediately try to resolve it. And we can resolve it one of two ways. One way is to own up to the negative act and address the harm caused by it.* **The other way is to justify the negative act rather than admit any wrong doing**

(Dr Joy DeGruy Leary: Post Traumatic Slave Syndrome - 2005)

**What is the difference between Diversity and Equality of Opportunity?**

It is important to be clear about the difference between these two ideas because it is all too convenient for us to say:

- What is diversity?
- I don't really understand what EOP and diversity are?
- I am diverse, I haven't got a prejudiced bone in my body!
- Why are we bothering with this? We are all equal......

To come from a place of saying '*I do not understand!*' is not good enough, especially considering we work within diverse teams and engage with a diverse service user group. For us to plead ignorance around this important subject matter that should be a thought provoking journey for a professional to take, is not acceptable. Diversity awareness can improve outcomes for service users and team cohesion through a mature and challenging approach to difference.

| Equal Opportunities | Managing Diversity |
|---|---|
| ▪ Concentrates on issues of discrimination<br>▪ Is perceived as an issue for women, ethnic minorities and people with disabilities<br>▪ Places less emphasis on culture change and more on the meeting of business objectives<br>▪ Is seen as an issue to do with personal and human resource practitioners | ▪ Ensures all employees maximise their potential and their contribution to the organisation<br>▪ Embraces a broad range of people; no one is excluded<br>▪ Concentrates on issues of<br>movement in an organisation,<br>the culture of the organisation, and meeting business objectives<br>▪ Is the concern of all employees, especially managers<br>▪ Does not rely on positive action/affirmative action |

*(Adapted from The Effective Manager, Perspective and Illustrations, ed. Jon Billberry, Sage Publications, London, 1996)*

The table above in many ways says that Equality of Opportunities is driven by policy and legislative requirements. However, diversity is driven by the **willingness** of the individual and the team. This 'willingness' to explore oneself and a team around the issue of diversity can be described as a building block to view the world a little differently.

## What Shapes Diversity?

Dr. Joy Leary developed a deservedly excellent reputation when she revisited the already known concept of cognitive dissonance, i.e. how we process and consciously, or unconsciously, justify negative values and behaviour towards particular social groups. She touched on something called 'the heart of the matter'. *The heart of the matter,* is a scary prospect for an individual or team to acknowledge because of the internalised discomfort it causes, hence the need to rationalise a justification for our actions. It is important to realise that the justification can be acted out by the professional, through theories and in the development of policy.

A tool that explores the meaning of diversity is the **dimensions framework.** It states that there are three dimensions to diversity:

1. Dimensions that tend to be shaped by birth:
   - I am heterosexual
   - I am male
   - I am Japanese

128

- I am a son or daughter
- I was born into a devout Catholic family etc.

These are things over which we have no control over, things that we were born with and into.

2. Dimensions influenced by the historical moments and eras of a person's life:

- Becoming a father for the first time
- Losing one's virginity
- Going to college
- Starting school

3. These are moments that may have imprinted themselves upon us because when they happened they helped to shape our view of the world; dimensions that evolve through a persons life.

- Being a father
- Exploring one's spirituality
- Being a husband or a wife
- Enjoying reggae music etc.

These are things that grow through one's life, which are ongoing and reflect who we are.

**Dimension Chart:**

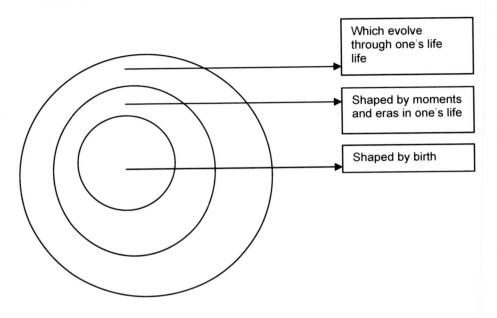

| | | Which evolve through one's life life |
| | | Shaped by moments and eras in one's life |
| | | Shaped by birth |

## Exercise

| Dimensions | Individual 1 | Individual 2 | Individual 3 | Individual 4 |
|---|---|---|---|---|
| Shaped by birth | White British Female Bi-sexual Only daughter Born in Bolton Roman Catholic | Indian Male Heterosexual Eldest son Born in India Hindu | White English Male Heterosexual Youngest of 5 children No real religion Hearing disability | Nigeri an Female Christian Eldest Daughter |

| Shaped by historical moments or eras in one's life | Going to college Getting divorced Giving birth Losing virginity Stopping drinking Bereavement | Independence Is Dyslexic Coming to UK Studying Bereavement of both parents Becoming a Father | Going to school | Coming to London at 10 Learning English Going to School Bullying Giving Birth |
|---|---|---|---|---|
| Which evolve through one's life | Studying Motherhood Atheism Sexuality | Relationship with his religion Being the family head Studying | Managing loneliness | Spirituality Getting Old |

## What happens when these individuals come together?

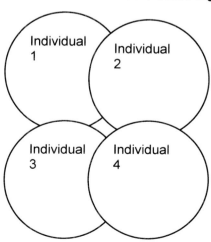

How unwise it would be to say that when these individuals come together, there will be **harmony.** It would be wiser for an individual, a team, a service and an organisation etc. to say that this potentially poses a major problem and it is a problem that if not addressed can be extremely damaging. As a drugs professional, whether you are a:

- Drugs Professional
- Psychiatrist
- Nurse
- Social Worker
- Probation Officer
- DIP Worker
- Outreach Worker
- Youth Worker
- Policy Maker etc.

**You are not immune to the issues of diversity.**

Note: we have added a fourth circle which represents a dimension focusing on regional, national and intergenerational history i.e. the reason the Irish and English communities struggle at times is because England and Southern and Northern Ireland have had an inter-linked history that is hundreds of years old. And this still has an influence on the here and now. This shapes how each group views the other and how one group acts towards the other. In many ways this discussion is:

**That simple and straight forward!**

Again our contemporary relationship with disability, sexuality etc. derives from our earliest history when mankind first formed social groups. And this history is what shapes belief and attitudes in the present day.

***Relationship between diversity and interventions for crack cocaine users:***

For many reasons crack cocaine has presented a formidable problem to drugs professionals across the board. Why:

- have services taken so long to materialise for crack cocaine service users?
- do we say that this drug simply affects the service user psychologically?
- is this drug predominantly associated with black people?
- are the interventions used for this service user group lacking in any real understanding of crack cocaine?
- do practitioners talk as though they are pharmacologists?
- since the drug became known, has it taken 25 years to develop poor to mediocre services?
- are major interventions for this service user group found within criminal justice and mental health services?

Services and training have most likely been developed from a protestant, middle class, Eurocentric and pseudo-scientific perspective.

## What next?

We need also to acknowledge the **'isms'** that are fundamental to our everyday society, and we must be able to discuss these questions and manage our own discomfort in the process. A good structural engineer will be very aware of the foundations s/he is constructing a building upon.   This has to come first, and it **must be taken seriously**.   It cannot be allowed to fall into the 'too difficult' box. Diversity is first and foremost about self-awareness, and then about the desire to make appropriate changes.

# *Chapter Nine*

## Congruence

An interesting aspect of communication is how or to what degree, we 'agree' with something or someone. It is important that as drugs professionals we understand this process of agreeing or disagreeing with something or someone. If we do not own, or admit to, our agreement or disagreement with someone then that interaction/communication is inherently flawed and therefore invalid, because the communication itself was in some sense dishonest. When a communication is dishonest (for whatever reason), we have a tendency to:

**Leak!**

In the context of this discussion, leaking refers to:

*Something that permits the emission or escape of 'something else',*
*usually with prejudicial effect!*
*(Webster Dictionary: 1981)*

Naturally, leaking can be highly destructive, and fundamentally prevents effective communication. Honesty should not be expressed in a negative way i.e. *'that's your opinion!'* It is an important aspect of communication simply because it can reduce the 'leaking' syndrome. Should the word 'honesty' be used? We think it has a place because most, if not all of us, have an opinion as to whether someone's words are, 'authentic' or not. It is however, crucial to word your 'honest' feedback in an appropriate way. It is not an excuse or justification for rudeness. Honesty tests not only our skill as communicators but also our core values. It is about developing the ability to disagree, confront and challenge with respect and without prejudice. It is the art of addressing sensitive issues without undermining or attacking the other person's dignity and sense of self. What we must not do is **avoid** our **'honest'** feelings in our communication with someone, in this case a service user.

**What is congruence?**

*To be in harmony with, in agreement with, aligned with….*
**The opposite (incongruence) being:**
*Not being in harmony with…*

Our understanding of how we manage incongruence within ourselves as drugs professionals, will dictate in many ways, how well we manage it with the service user. It can also stop us from:

***Wasting a lot of time!***

*Rogers states:*

*'The more the therapist is himself or herself in the relationship, putting up no professional front or personal facade, the greater is the likelihood that the client will change and grow in a constructive*

136

*manner. This means that the therapist is 'openly being the feelings and attitudes' that are flowing within (him/her) at the moment.*

*The term "transparent" catches the flavour of this condition: the therapist makes himself or herself transparent to the client; the client can see right through the therapist within their relationship; the client experiences no holding back on the part of the therapist. As for the therapist, what he or she is experiencing is available to awareness, can be lived in the relationship, and can be communicated, **if appropriate**. Thus, there is a close matching, or congruence, between what is being experienced at the **gut level**, i.e, what is present in awareness, and what is expressed to the client.'*

*(Carl R. Rogers. Way of Being. Boston: Houghton Mifflin, 1980, p.115-116)*

Many of us work contary to the above and although we are not suggesting that this is the best or only way to work with a service user, there are some interesting statements in the quotation from Rogers which are worth exploring:

| |
|---|
| ■ '……the therapist is openly **being** the feelings and **attitudes** that are **flowing within** him/her at the moment.' |
| ■ 'The term "transparent" catches the flavour of this condition' |
| ■ 'As for the therapist, what he or she is experiencing is available to awareness, can be lived in the relationship, and |

> can be communicated, **if appropriate**.'

- 'Thus, there is a close matching, or congruence, between what is being experienced **at the gut level**, what is present in awareness, and what is expressed to the client.'

The degree of self awareness and self questioning required in order to work in this way would be considerable. Why? Because Rogers mentions being in touch **at a gut level!** Is he asking us to be honest, in order to develop a congruent relationship with the service user? Is he saying that the service user is very aware of 'us' whether we wear a nurse's uniform, a drugs workers uniform or a doctor's white coat? He appears to recognise that the 'service user' is as aware of the professional, as the 'professional' is of the service user, which means that the **interaction** of the drugs professional with the service user is **crucial**.

Let us also remember that Rogers stresses 'appropriate' i.e. he does not appear to be saying that the professional should be spilling out their life history to the service user but he does appear to be advocating that the professional should be aware of what is going on within them with regards to the service user. Whether the service user says anything to the professional about how they view him/her, the conundrum of the professional's behaviour is still there! As professional drugs workers we often use our 'professionalism' as a badge or alter-ego, almost like 'Super Man's' cape! Wearing Super Man's cape has its benefits, but it can create numerous problems in the work environment!

138

A drugs professional clearly has a role, and that role differentiates the professional from the service user. However, the professional's awareness of their feelings towards the service user is still vital.

## Can congruence be mistaken or confused?

Yes it can, if the drugs professional is harmonised or identifying with the wrong thing within the service user. For example, the professional can become confused, and therefore incongruent with the needs of the service user. In the world of psychology and psycho-therapy terminology such as counter transference, projected identification, etc. are used. No matter how it is worded professionals are regularly aligning themselves to the service user in the wrong way *because they are ignoring their own projections!*

- ➢ I am a female worker
- ➢ The female service user has been abused, therefore I will be able to relate to her best because I am also female

- ➢ The client was in an abusive relationship
- ➢ S/he needs to get out of the relationship because the partner is the reason s/he uses the drug.

- ➢ Crack creates rapid dependency
- ➢ How can you stop using any drug that is that so addictive?

- ➢ I know where you are coming from.
- ➢ Because I used drugs and I can relate to you.

- You were sexually abused.
- So that's why you use drugs. I would do the same thing if that had happened to me.

**Professionals need to be mindful of why they have such a strong allegiance to a particular client.**

Congruence is at the heart of how we view, interact with and inform the service user as to whether we 'like' them or not. Of course to 'like' or 'dislike' a service user is clearly unacceptable and unprofessional. Equally, to say 'I am 'scared' of that service user' is generally unaccepted because of the shield provided by the label of 'professional!'

The idea of congruence and incongruence manifests itself around the service user in physical behaviour, verbal tone and body language. These are aspects of the professional that they cannot hide and of which the service user is aware. How the professional understands themselves in relation to the service user is vital because the more the professional can recognise how they feel and act towards the service user, the more they can understand the static that exists at times, between them. This generates a greater degree of **honesty** at the heart of the relationship between the drugs professional and the service user. The question is, how can we explore congruence in a meaningful way?

## Congruence and Non Verbal Communication (NVC)

Non Verbal Communication is at the heart of communication because it is such a difficult thing to disguise or hide, unless of course you have received special MI5 training! Non Verbal Communication is one of the most obvious and ever-present displays of feeling from one human being to another.

### *What is non verbal communication?*

Non verbal communication is something we all do on a day to day basis. It is often classified as being subtle and is viewed as difficult to prove. This is contradictory to the attitude of the Police to NVC, or intelligence agencies to NVC, or psychologists' and advertisers' responses to NVC! Why do these groups take it so seriously while professionals who work with marginalized groups have difficulty with it? The reason could well be the fact that they recognise that NVC is one of the truest forms of transmitting how one feels.

**Body language** is a term for communication using body movements or gestures (such as the **Pinocchio Syndrome**) instead of, or in addition to sounds, verbal language or other forms of communication. It belongs in the category of paralanguage, which describes all forms of human communication that are not verbal language. This includes the most subtle of movements that many people are not aware of, including winking and slight movements of the eyebrows. In addition body language can also incorporate the use of facial expressions.

Paralanguage, including body language, has been extensively studied in <u>social psychology</u>. In common parlance and <u>popular psychology</u> the term is most often applied to body language that is considered involuntary, even though the distinction between voluntary and involuntary body language is often controversial. For example, a <u>smile</u> may be produced either <u>consciously</u> or unconsciously.

(Wiki-pedia 2007)


**Paralanguage**

Paralanguage refers to tones and intonations and more, which are a part of speech yet may well be saying something quite different to the words coming from the mouth of the speaker. How the words are delivered have subtle and not so subtle inferences that create **discord** in the listener if the words coming from the mouth of the speaker do not coincide with the other components that make up oral communication. How we use these 'other' characteristics of language are as unconscious as they are conscious and the speaker may well be unaware of what they are doing. These 'other' aspects of language are classified as 'non-verbal' communication.

*Example:*

The different meanings within a sentence depending on what is emphasized:

142

- **She's** giving this money to me.

  SHE is the one giving the money, nobody else.
- She's **giving** this money to me.

  She is GIVING, not lending.
- She's giving this **money** to me.

  MONEY is being exchanged, not anything else.
- She's giving this money to **me**.

  I am getting the money, nobody else.

(Web Author: Stephanie Gragg: Date Published 11.12.01)

The reason why paralanguage provides something very interesting and special in our communication with the service user is because **no one,** including professionals, is immune to how s/he uses intonation, stress, pitch, pause, resonance etc., and these all transmit particular and specific messages to the service user. How we communicate with the service user whether it be conscious or unconscious will dictate how the service user **views and relates to us!** Honesty, in a safe, trained way, is crucial because, if the professional does not have self awareness around how they communicate with the service user, they will correctly be viewed, even if it is not verbalised, as a 'liar'.

Paralanguage will demonstrate to the service user whether or not we:

- Trust them
- Like them
- Fear them
- Feel disgusted by them

- Are attracted to them etc.

*The voice is an extraordinary human instrument. Every time we speak, our voice reveals our gender, age, geographic background, level of education, native birth (culture), emotional state, and our relationship with the person spoken to. All these clues (and many more) are contained in even small fragments of speech, and other people can "read" our voices with remarkable accuracy. When we speak, we **"encode"** important information about **ourselves**; when we listen to others, we can **"decode"** important information about **them**.*

*(John Gumperz, Professor of Anthropology, UC Berkley, author of Discourse Strategies)*

Paralanguage is intricately connected to body language.

**Body Language**

Body language refers to the full range of physical movement and responses to particular situations. These manifest in the form of conscious and unconscious gestures. A gesture is when a part of the body, such as the hand, legs, eyes etc. is used in conjunction with, or instead of, verbal communication. Through gestures the individual is able to demonstrate a vast range of feelings and deep opinions of agreement and disagreement.

**A smile**

| This represents a forced smile, in which only the muscles are involved in the smiling process. FALSE | This represents a natural smile, in which many muscle groups around the face move involuntarily. The cheeks crunch up the eyes squeeze together. HONEST |

A simple smile denotes whether someone is being honest with you, whether they find your joke funny, and whether they are happy to see you. The above could be used around the expression of:

- Fear
- Sadness
- Loathing
- Respect

- Tolerance
- Patience etc.

And the above only refers to the face, not to mention the other means of body language that the drugs professional might use such as the hands and arms, the stance and the breath.

## Congruence, Non Verbal Communication and the Crack Cocaine User

All the aforementioned and more, reveal how we feel about a service user. The crack cocaine service user challenges many aspects of the objectivity the professional aims to show to this cohort of drug users. Professionals were initially conditioned to believe that the crack cocaine service user is:

- Aggressive
- Prone to mood swings
- Prone to mental health issues, in the form of 'crack psychosis' etc.

Another association that was made, is that crack cocaine use is most prevalent within the Afro-Caribbean community, and out of this association, a cultural stereotype was born. Could it be that professionals when engaging with the crack user are so conditioned to the perception of the addictive and problematic nature of this service user group that their non verbal communication with the client, suggests that the service user is essentially 'very problematic'? This could represent a non verbal communication response based on fear, and as a result, that this service user needs to be controlled and contained, or even that we do not want this type of person in our service.

Congruence is important in understanding how we feel about the service user. It is crucial that we understand ourselves, and how our experiences, socialisation and education unavoidably influence how we regard, relate to and interact with service users in a potentially damaging way.

Remember, congruence does not simply refer to the professionals' interaction with the service user, it also refers to the services' response to the service user. Workers and services have been incongruent with the crack service user for a long time and this has determined the slow progression in the development of effective services. Understanding congruence and its relationship to paralanguage and body language can only aid us in our understanding of our relationship with service users in general and the crack cocaine service user in particular.

# Chapter Ten

## How people learn?

Janus Solutions is eclectic in how it views interventions for crack cocaine service users, and in truth, all drug users. Is it wise for us to inform someone that this is the best way to learn, or should we be observing a service user and then ask ourselves:

*What is the best way to communicate information to **this individual?***

and

*How can we make learning **accessible** to **this individual?***

It is also very important to view how we learn from a diversity perspective. All too often, as professional drugs workers we transmit knowledge in a way that is comfortable and familiar to us, but not necessarily familiar to the service user. This is a huge assumption and ultimately, a major problem, because we all learn in different ways. This can cut across gender, disability, race and culture, language, vocabulary, educational background and educational experience, religious sense of oneself and one's philosophical view of oneself and the world etc. We state very clearly here, that the issue is not with the theoretical frameworks or the service user, but with the professionals within the field of substance use. If we wish to maximise the effectiveness of interventions for the crack cocaine user we need to think and approach the issue of learning in a very different way. In order to explore this more fully let us look at an educational tool called the:

## Learning Style Inventory and Multiple Intelligence Approach

David A. Kolb's Learning Style Inventory describes the way we learn and how we deal with ideas and day-to-day situations in our lives (Experiential Learning 1984), and the multiple intelligence approach by David Lazear (*Seven Ways of Knowing: Teaching for Multiple Intelligences* by David Lazear. 1991.) looks at how people learn.

## Learning styles: a multiple intelligence approach

Multiple Intelligence (MI) theory asserts that there are many paths to learning. It makes reference to seven ways of learning yet acknowledges that there could be more still. MI states that there are "seven intelligences":

- body/kinesthetic
- interpersonal
- intra-personal
- logical/mathematical
- musical/rhythmic
- verbal/linguistic
- visual/spatial

The approach does not say that people cannot learn and develop skills in the other intelligences, however it does suggest that within our current frameworks of learning in the western world, two forms of intelligence dominate the 'ways of learning', and they are:

150

- Logical/mathematical and
- Verbal/linguistic

## Body/Kinesthetic Intelligence

This intelligence is related to physical movement and the knowing/wisdom of the body including the brain's motor cortex, which controls bodily motion. Body/kinesthetic intelligence is awakened through physical movement for example various sports, dance, and physical exercises as well as by the expression of oneself through the body, such as inventing, drama, body language, and creative/interpretative dance.

*Capacities involved:*

*control of "voluntary" movements*

*control of "pre-programmed" movements*

*expanding awareness through the body*

*the mind and body connection*

*mimetic abilities*

*improved body functioning*

*Multiple Intelligences by David Lazear. 1991*

## Interpersonal Intelligence

This intelligence operates primarily through person-to-person relationships and communication. Interpersonal intelligence is activated by person-to-person encounters in which effective

151

communication, working together with others for a common goal, and noticing distinctions among persons are necessary and important.

*Capacities involved:*

*effective verbal/non-verbal communication*

*sensitivity to others' moods, temperaments, motivations, and feelings*

*Working cooperatively in a group*

*ability to discern others' underlying intentions and behaviour*

*"passing over" into the perspective of another*

*creating and maintaining synergy*

*Multiple Intelligences by David Lazear. 1991.*

### Intra-personal Intelligence

This intelligence relates to inner states of being, self-reflection, metacognition (i.e. thinking about thinking), and awareness of spiritual realities. Intra-personal intelligence is awakened when we are in situations that cause introspection and require knowledge of the internal aspects of the self, such as awareness of our feelings, thinking processes, self-reflection, and spirituality.

152

*Capacities involved:*

*concentration of the mind*

*Mindfulness*

*Metacognition*

*awareness and expression of different feelings*

*transpersonal sense of the self*

*higher-order thinking and reasoning*

*Multiple Intelligences by David Lazear. 1991.*

### Logical/Mathematical Intelligence

Often called "scientific thinking," this intelligence deals with inductive and deductive thinking/reasoning, numbers, and the recognition of abstract patterns. Logical mathematical intelligence is activated in situations requiring problem solving or meeting a new challenge as well as situations requiring pattern discernment and recognition.

*Capacities involved:*

*abstract pattern recognition*

*inductive reasoning*

*deductive reasoning*

*discerning relationships & connections*

*performing complex calculations*

*scientific reasoning*

*Multiple Intelligences by David Lazear. 1991.*

## Musical/Rhythmic Intelligence

This intelligence is based on the recognition of tonal patterns, including various environmental sounds, and on a sensitivity to rhythm and beat. Musical/rhythmic intelligence is turned on by the resonance or 'vibrational' effect of music and rhythm on the brain, including such things as the human voice, sounds from nature, musical instruments, percussion instruments, and other humanly produced sounds.

*Capacities involved:*

*appreciation of the structure of music*

*schemes or frames in the mind for hearing music*

*sensitivity to sounds*

*recognition, creation, and reproduction of melody/rhythm*

*sensing characteristic qualities of tone*

*Multiple Intelligences by David Lazear. 1991.*

## Verbal/Linguistic Intelligence

This intelligence, which is related to words and language, both written and spoken, dominates most Western educational systems. Verbal linguistic intelligence is awakened by the spoken word, by reading someone's ideas, thoughts, or poetry, or by writing one's own ideas, thoughts, or poetry, as well as by various kinds of humour such as "plays on words," jokes, and "twists" of the language.

154

*Capacities
involved:*

*understanding order & meaning of words*

*convincing someone of a course of action*

*explaining, teaching, and learning*

*humour*

*memory & recall*

*"meta-linguistic" analysis*

*Multiple Intelligences by David Lazear. 1991.*

## Visual/Spatial Intelligence

This intelligence, which relies on the sense of sight and being able to visualize an object, includes the ability to create internal mental images/pictures. Visual/spatial intelligence is triggered by presenting the mind with creating unusual, delightful, and colourful designs, patterns, shapes, and pictures, and engaging in active imagination through such things as visualization, guided imagery, and pretend exercises.

*Capacities
involved:*

*active imagination*

*Forming mental images*

*finding your way in space*

*image manipulations*

*graphic representation*

*recognizing relationships of objects in space*

155

*accurate perception from different angles*

*Multiple Intelligences by David Lazear. 1991.*

It is crucial to remember that as drugs professionals we do not leave the wider world behind us when we deliver interventions to primary crack cocaine or other drug service users. The same inclusive approach should be applied as with other fields of work. Furthermore, we have the opportunity to learn from other disciplines; from their creativity and innovation as well as from their mistakes. Educational psychology clearly emphasises that we have different learning attribution states which as professionals, services, organisations, commissioners, policy and strategy leads etc., we should be aware of when we go about our business of work. Our inclination should always be one of trying to improve our level of communication with the service user.

This is something that many of us would intuitively agree with. However, in the world of 'evidence based practice' the intuitive side of service development is superseded by the 'rational' aspect of ourselves. The sad thing is, that as professionals we may also only use **two types** of our own **learning intelligence!**

If we are advocating an eclectic approach to delivering information, we are recognising that without it, our ability to reach as many service users as possible is hugely decreased, because some of them, depending on their learning makeup and diverse backgrounds will not be able to process the information we are trying to impart.

156

*No intervention is perfect, however, as providers and designers of services the goal is simply to get quality improved outcomes for the service user.*

# Chapter Eleven

## How people communicate

How helpful is the language we use within the drugs field? When we engage a crack cocaine user, how mindful should we be of the type and context of the language we use? You may be aware throughout this book that we have used the description 'service user' when referring to the crack cocaine user. We have not used the terminology:

- Addict
- Patient
- Junkie/crackhead etc.

The use of language, in relation to drug use, whether the professional uses it overtly, or the drugs professional uses it in a hidden discreet manner, will influence both how the client views themselves and how the professional views the client. Consider this question:

*How did you learn your drugs work language and beliefs?*

Within the drugs field there is a proliferation of language such as: junkie, scag-head, crack-head, clean, addict, wired, psychosis, paranoid, aggressive etc. Where does this language come from? How helpful is it? How does it affect the service user? How does it

159

influence how the service user views themselves? What is the positive and negative impact of language on the service user? How is the relationship between the professional and the service user shaped by their use of language?

Much of the language that we use in relation to the service user may act like a loaded gun to their treatment.

- *Crack, bad, mad, black*
- *Crack baby etc.*

In order to understand language we have to strip it down to the bone to give it its true, profound and influencing worth!

**Persuasive Language**

A good platform for this is Persuasive Language. Persuasive language has both healthy and unhealthy connotations when used around substance users and crack cocaine service users in particular. It is essential for professionals to recognise that how we view the crack cocaine user did not simply come through objective and 'true' evidence based research. As professionals we were also shaped by external influences.

We wish to be more imaginative than simply saying we should not:

- Stereotype
- Be judgemental etc.

160

Persuasive Language offers us an interesting and hopefully thought provoking exploration on the power of oral and written communication.

*When you seek to convince, persuade or otherwise change other people's minds, the language you use is extremely important. Each word is a little packet of meaning from which the other person* infers *understanding. It gets even more complex when words combine in the semantics of entire sentences.*

When an individual infers they suggest:

....something which follows as certainly or probably true....
(Websters dictionary...)

*When an individual draws a conclusion, something more powerful than an inference takes place:*

A **conclusion** is stronger than an inference; it shuts us up to the result, and terminates inquiry. We **infer** what is particular or probable; we **conclude** what is certain.

(Websters dictionary...)

*The reason we are referring to 'infer' and 'conclude' is because when we are communicating about a service user or a specific type of service user i.e. a crack cocaine service user, if we have already come to a conclusion within ourselves about the nature of this client then we terminate the need for further investigation, and that* *investigation can mean the difference between **a good service** and **a bad service.***

*Our inferences and conclusions are not necessarily shaped by evidence, facts, authentic data etc. Inferences and conclusions are, or can be shaped by:*

- *History*
- *One's own previous experience*
- *Our personal and learnt belief system*
- *Our value systems*
- *Our view of the world etc.*

## What is the framework for persuasive language?

| Some Components of Persuasive Language | |
|---|---|
| *Empathy* | Encouraging the reader or listener to imagine a situation, usually one in which someone is suffering. |
| *Rhetorical Question* | A question asked by the text or speaker that does not require an answer. They are used to encourage the reader or listener to think. |
| *Rule of three: Triadic Structure* | Three words, clauses or sentences given together in order to create a memorable impact. |

162

| | |
|---|---|
| *Adjectives* | Words that describe nouns, such as **'big'** **'blue'** or **'nasty'**. |
| *Metaphors* | A comparison of two terms using the words **'IS'** or **'ARE'**. **E.g. this room is a *pig stye*!** |
| *Powerful Imagery* | Using language to create mental pictures, usually with a powerful or emotional theme. |
| *Semantic Fields* | Groups of words all relating to the same topic. |
| *Direct Interactions with the reader or listener* | Speaking to the reader directly in a text, for example by using the pronoun **'YOU'**. |
| *Inclusive Tones* | A technique to make the reader feel part of a text, for example, using **'WE'** or **'US'**. |
| *Demonstrative Pronouns* | Words that are used to demonstrate or show the reader something to make them feel **'close'** to a text. Common examples are **'this'** and **'these'**. |

## Comparison: using the persuasive framework

### 'I have a dream' by Martin Luther King

| Components of Persuasive Language | |
|---|---|
| **Repetition (It's powerful):** | |
| **I have a dream** | that one day this nation will rise up and live out the true meaning of its creed: "We hold these truths to be self-evident: that all men are created equal." |
| **I have a dream** | that one day on the red hills of Georgia the sons of former slaves and the sons of former slave owners will be able to sit down together at a table of brotherhood. |
| **I have a dream** | that my four children will one day live in a nation where they will not be judged by the colour of their skin but by the content of their character. |
| **Adjectives:** | ...will be transformed into a situation where **little black boys** and **black girls** will be able to join hands with **little white boys** and **white girls** and walk together as sisters and brothers... |

| Inclusive tones | ...When **we** let freedom ring, when **we** let it ring from every village and every hamlet, from every state and every city, **we** will be able to speed up that day when all of God's children, black men and white men, Jews and Gentiles, Protestants and Catholics, will be able to join hands and sing in the words of the old Negro spiritual, "Free at last! Free at last!  Thank God Almighty, **we** are free at last!" |
| --- | --- |
| | This momentous decree came as a **great beacon light of hope** to millions of Negro slaves who had been **seared in the flames of withering injustice**. It came as a **joyous daybreak to end the long night of captivity**... |

**Crack cocaine language**

**When considering this, think of newspapers, radio and television**

| Components of Persuasive Language | |
|---|---|
| BBC Article:  Monday, 24 June, 2002, 21:11 GMT 22:11 UK | |
| **Repetition:**<br><br>**Gangs** | The leader ......said that **gangs** importing the drug, often from Jamaica, are clearly linked to gun crime in Britain and must be stopped. |
| **Gangs** | In Scotland the Drugs Enforcement Agency reported a threefold increase in seizures of heroin and cocaine and claims it had disrupted more than 70 **gangs.** |
| **Gangs** | He said the trade's links to Jamaican **gangs** "cannot be ignored" and warned that lives were being put at risk by the practice of using 'drugs mules', who smuggle crack into Britain by swallowing packages. |
| **Adjectives** | ..levels of **violence** are hitting........the levels of **violence** with the black community are quite extraordinary......it's certainly associated with more |

| | |
|---|---|
| | **violent crime** and particular thefts, than robberies and burglaries……. |
| Senator Charles Schumer: http://en.wikipedia.org/wiki/Crack_epidemic | |
| **Powerful Imagery** | Twenty years ago, crack was headed east across the United States like a **Mack Truck out of control**, and it **slammed New York hard** because we just didn't see the warning signs. |
| **Powerful Imagery** | The Drug Enforcement Agency officially classifies the **time of the epidemic** starting in 1984 and ending in 1990, in what can be considered to be the **height of the epidemic**. |

The above speeches and articles demonstrate how we are influenced by 'persuasive language'. Persuasive language is something, which permeates our conscious and unconscious selves. It influences and directs policy, it influences treatment direction and it influences how we view the service user.

As we evolve in our professional roles we must understand the nature of communication, both from the perspective that *communication affects us, and in turn how our communication affects the service user.*

- **When you hear:  Gang!**
    - *What do you associate it with?  What comes up for you?*

- **When you hear:  Violence!**
    - *What do you associate it with?  What comes up for you?*

- **When you hear:  'out of control' 'slammed New York hard!**
    - *What do you associate it with?  What comes up for you?*

- **When you hear:  Epidemic!**
    - *What do you associate it with?  What comes up for you?*

*This list goes on.  It fundamentally affects how professionals and services perceive the crack cocaine service user, in the most profound manner.*

**What are the benefits of understanding the constituent parts of Persuasive Language?**

*As mentioned, persuasive language is something used by orators to transmit a message in a powerful and affecting way.  The orator uses*

168

words almost like a mathematical formula that resembles a wave. That wave washes over and touches the listener in a very special way. It affects the individual because:

- Words and statements are repeated
- The listener identifies with the words and subject matter
- The descriptive words supporting the subject matter create such a powerful image that the listener cannot help but be swayed by them
- Our deepest emotions can be triggered by particular words making the image long lasting
- The listener requires something to hold on to

Some individuals appear to have communication skills intuitively, others study them, however, the most important point of this discussion is that for professionals these are tools that we can use in the workplace. All that the professional and the team have to do is:

- be mindful of their language
- develop the team's collective use of language and
- guide the service users use of language.

Persuasive Language is a skill and a tool that can be used in:

- a healthy enabling way or
- an unhelpful disabling way

# Chapter Twelve

## Contemporary Models

This section provides a brief outline of the therapeutic interventions most commonly used in working with crack cocaine users. This will allow us the opportunity to get a sense of what is being offered to crack cocaine users, while at the same time considering the effectiveness of these interventions on the crack cocaine user. These theories are described in brief and are therefore merely points of reference for workers. We do believe that it is important for drugs professionals to have a good understanding of the theoretical frameworks that underpin the most commonly used interventions. While we do not show a preference for any one particular theory, we do advocate that it is important for drugs professionals to know from which theories their core working principles and rationale arise.

There are many schools of thought and practice regarding psycho-therapeutic interventions. Due to the nature and prevalence of substance misuse a number of theories have been identified as relevant to generating a treatment plan when working the substance misuser. C Kouimtsidis and M. T. Abou-Saleh (1999) identified a plethora of therapeutic interventions, namely, the 12-step approach most favoured by Narcotics Anonymous and its alcohol equivalent; Dynamic Psychotherapy, based on Freud's view of addiction, i.e. addiction is due to underlying neurosis; Supportive-Expressive Therapy, focusing on transference-counter-transference, resistance, the relationship with therapist and taking responsibility; Interpersonal Therapy, exploring expression, clarification and communication, education around modelling etc. Carroll et al (1987) identifies Psychotherapy as the one consistent intervention used by services in the treatment of stimulant use, and in particular cocaine use.

## *Education*

Carroll et al (1987), while studying the work of Gawin and Kebler (1986) identified that clear, precise and truthful information can be an effective tool for allaying the fears and anxieties of cocaine users. This is especially the case when the cocaine user is experiencing a plethora of effects and side effects, most obviously the euphoria, the crash and subsequent **anhedonia** (an inability to gain pleasure from normal enjoyable experiences) and the resultant cravings, which may be triggered by that desperate feeling, or lack of feeling. Through the process of education the service user may be better equipped to deal with the symptoms as and when they arise. As a result the stimulant user may better cope with lapse and relapse more effectively.

## **Psychodynamic Theory**

In the exploration of the theory of neurosis Freud (1900) suggests that trauma in childhood poses a threat to the ego. With the repressed memories (unpleasant) and emotions of the trauma, neurotic symptoms develop (coping strategies). Freud hypothesised that the **self** requires that the **id, ego** and **superego** function in a relatively balanced way. With regard to substance use, Freud believed that the problems of drug use were stimulated by underlying neuroses caused by past events. Freud argued that by treating the neurosis, an improvement in the management of an individual's substance issue would follow.

In Freudian Theory addictive behaviour is explained as fixation with, or regression to, the oral psychosexual stage that is characterised by dependence, inability to tolerate frustration and unwillingness to delay gratification. Such frustrations motivate the individual to pursue oral gratification through the consumption of alcohol or drugs. Sometimes defence mechanisms or rationalisations are adopted which serve to protect the coping function of the ego, that is to say:

*'I drink to forget a traumatic event in my past'* – the emotional trauma from the past event is as a result transferred elsewhere. The result is: *'My problem is depression not drinking'*. This then becomes the rationalisation for the substance use.

## Interpersonal Psychotherapy

Here there is an emphasis on the individual's interaction with other people, particularly on issues such as interpersonal disputes, role transitions, and interpersonal deficits. Techniques used are:

- exploration methods
- clarification and communication analysis

These coupled with educational and advice tools, aim to help the individual to come to terms with change. Change through self exploration and clarification of their actions to themselves and others will lead to the individual re-evaluating his or her relationship with his or her drug of choice.

## Psychodynamic Counselling

Psychodynamic theory suggests that substance use is a form of self medication regarding *painful affect states* (Khantzian 1985; Krystal and Raskin 1970; Weder and Kaplan 1969). With supportive-expressive therapy the focus of the facilitator and the client is to explore conflict states and how these conflict states affect our interpersonal and intra-personal relationships. Carroll (1987) postulates that supportive-expressive treatments for cocaine users offer an environment whereby the therapist tries to support certain aspects of the patient's personality while at the same time exploring other aspects of the patient in more depth. The approach aims at encouraging the client to focus on two primary goals, one being abstinence the other being an exploration of the interpersonal and intra-personal conflicts at the root of the addictive behaviour. As a result the area which focuses on abstinence is more directive, allowing the therapist space to encourage strategies to enable long lasting abstinence, developing the clients self esteem etc. However, for issues such as childhood trauma the therapist will be neutral, interpretive and non-directive.

For the service user engaging in this type of intervention, it would be made clear that their substance use (crack cocaine use) is a symptom of deeper issues.

174

Currently there is much interest in two psychotherapeutic treatments that have come to the forefront of psychological treatments. These are Motivational Interviewing and Cognitive Behavioural Therapy. Much hope has been placed on these two interventions for working with the crack cocaine service user. For W R Miller and S Rollnick (1991) the developers of Motivational Interviewing, its essential feature revolves around a familiar theme, that of 'change'. For Miller and Rollnick (1991) the basis of the theory is one that looks at *ambivalence* and the battle between *indulgence* and *restraint*. These are seen as easily identified symptoms of addictive behaviour that often block the process of change in an individual. Within MI the issue of resistance to change, which is seen within certain frameworks of therapeutic treatment as an almost deliberate act of trying *not* to change, is handled in a different way. MI has a place set aside for the 'resistant' client. The suggestion is that the motivation for an individual to change is sometimes affected by factors outside the client's control. MI also uses the cycle of change (J Prochaska and C Di Clemente's 1982) as a tool, which sees re/lapse as a natural phenomenon in the process of recovery. Ambivalence is, for the MI theorist, often described as the 'heart of the problem', something, which keeps the client stuck (Miller and Rollnick 1991). The aim of MI is to cause incongruence between the client and the addictive behaviour leading to a state whereby the client is led closer to a place of exploring change. The approach draws on Client-centred Counselling, Cognitive Therapy and the Social Psychology of Persuasion. It is described as a brief therapy because the therapist, even though remaining client centred, is at times directional, trying to shift the client from ambivalence and being 'stuck', to a place of 'movement' using clearly defined work tools.

Because personal control and responsibility are key to MI, they advocate the 'internal attribution state' whereby the client believes that they caused the change, rather than 'external attribution' which would suggest the change was caused by external factors.

In MI, motivation is seen as something that the therapist and the client work towards. It is not seen as a prerequisite to intervention. Denial is perceived as integral to the process of change rather than as a barrier to change and ambivalence is identified as the substance misuse problem, that the client must be encouraged to explore.

*The five areas of MI:*

- Express empathy
- Help client to recognise discrepancies between goals and current behaviour problem
- Avoid argument
- Roll with resistance rather than fight it
- Support self-efficacy by emphasising responsibility.

*MI draws on Prochaska and Di Clemente's **Cycle of Change:**.*

- Pre-contemplative
- Contemplative
- Determination
- Action
- Maintenance

176

## Cognitive Behavioural Therapy (CBT)

This model of therapy has its roots in work originally done around depression. It was developed by Professor Beck in the 1960s. In relation to substance misuse, the model identifies external stimuli for using i.e. socialising, partying etc., and internal stimuli i.e. emotional state and withdrawal (Kouimtsidis and Abou- Saleh 1999). Regarding drug use the substance user may feel that the desire to use is an automatic one, however the Cognitive Therapist would argue that the process of thought leading to the drug using was merely quick, giving the illusion of being automatic. In fact it was a fast thought making process on the part of the substance user, a thought making process that the therapist will encourage the client to become familiar with. Cravings and the ambivalence as to whether or not to use will accompany the process. The substance user will experience 'permission' thoughts that legitimise him/her to use eg. 'once won't hurt' and from this state the substance user will initiate a process of obtaining crack cocaine or other substances. The CBT therapist will use a variety of interventions to break this cycle including keeping a diary, imagery, looking at automatic thoughts, advantage/disadvantage analysis and drug beliefs etc. These allow for the substance user to explore his/her using process, leading to cognitive restructuring (Kouimtsidis and Abou-Saleh 1999).

## Relapse Prevention

As a psycho-social tool, relapse prevention has become a common strategy in the treatment of substance misuse generally. It has also been seen as a viable tool in the treatment of stimulant use because it can be easily applied to high risk situations and finding ways to cope with them. Marlatt & Gordon (1980) developed the ideas of relapse prevention into a workable tool that used cognitive-behavioural frameworks as techniques, that focused the individual on high risk situations that can lead to relapse. Through the process of self monitoring and behavioural analysis of substance use, the individual is able to use coping strategies, for the recognition of dangerous and problematic situations (Carroll 1997). A variety of tools could be used to explore these high risk situations, for example role play, homework etc, that enables the individual to become equipped to make informed choices.

## *Group Therapy*

Group therapy is seen by some as the most effective type of intervention, especially with cocaine users (Washton 1991). One of the benefits of group therapy is that groups can be facilitated not only by professionals but also by peers. The group provides a forum whereby the individual can gain support and education, learn to relate and be gently confronted by their peers about their drug use. In this setting defence mechanisms such as avoidance, denial and resistance can be explored. Due to the fact that stimulant users, cocaine users in particular, can experience a fear that they are unique in losing control over their behaviour, the process of being in a group can lead to a sense of universality and not feeling alone (Carroll 1987).

178

All of these theoretical approaches can be used to address the various aspects of drug dependence that include:

- Cravings
- Drug seeking behaviour
- Compulsivity
- Psychological Traps
- Pleasure

## Classical Conditioning and Operant Conditioning

The reason why there is a degree of focus on these two forms of looking at and controlling behaviour is because in many ways they represent the impact of a 'whole' service on an individual, and how a service or intervention may shape an individuals treatment.

### Classical Conditioning

### Learning by Association – Pavlov's Paradigm (Perspective):

Classical conditioning believes that behaviour can be learned and unlearnt. Drugs for the Behaviourist simply represent a form of behaviour that can be changed by engaging an individual in a behaviour modification programme, or set of prescriptive exercises. One of the stand alone examples of this is an experiment carried out by **Ivan Petrovich Pavlov** (September 14, 1849 – February 27, 1936) who was a Russian physiologist, psychologist, and physician. He was awarded the Nobel Prize in **Physiology or Medicine** in 1904 for research pertaining to the digestive system. Pavlov is widely known for first describing the phenomenon now known as Classical Conditioning in his experiments with dogs.

While Ivan Pavlov worked to unveil the secrets of the digestive system, he observed that when a dog encounters food it salivates. Saliva makes food easier to swallow, and the enzymes it contains help in the breakdown of food. When Pavlov was studying reflexes he observed that dogs drooled with the stimulus of food. He later discovered that the dogs were responding to the laboratory coat of the person bringing the food. Whenever the dogs saw a person wearing a laboratory coat they associated the coat with food. Developing this observation by introducing bells into the process, Pavlov observed that if the bell was sounded in close association with mealtimes, the dogs learned to associate food with the sound of the bell. Naturally if the bell was sounded without any food being present, the dogs still drooled.

### Application to Addictive Behaviour

Pavlov demonstrated that a conditioned response can lead to dependence through the process of associative learning. Specific stimuli through associative pairing with drugs or alcohol may lead to a sustained desire to use drugs or alcohol. Note: association may not only be with the 'high' but also with the memories, environment, equipment, ritual etc.

**Operant Conditioning**


**Operant Conditioning** is the term used by B.F. Skinner (1974) to describe the effects of the consequences of a particular behaviour on the future occurrence of that behaviour. There are four types of Operant Conditioning: Positive Reinforcement, Negative Reinforcement, Punishment and Extinction. Both Positive and Negative Reinforcement strengthen behaviour while both Punishment and Extinction weaken behaviour.

- In **Positive Reinforcement** a particular behaviour is strengthened by the consequence of experiencing a positive condition. For example:

  - A hungry rat presses a bar in its cage and receives food. The food is a positive condition for the hungry rat. The rat presses the bar again, and again receives food. The rat's behaviour of pressing the bar is strengthened by the consequence of receiving food.

- In **Negative Reinforcement** a particular behaviour is strengthened by the consequence of stopping or avoiding a negative condition. For example:

  - A rat is placed in a cage and immediately receives a mild electrical shock on its feet. The shock is a negative condition for the rat. The rat presses a bar and the shock stops. The rat receives another

181

shock, presses the bar again, and again the shock stops. The rat's behaviour of pressing the bar is strengthened by the consequence of stopping the shock.

- In **Punishment** a particular behaviour is weakened by the consequence of experiencing a negative condition. For example:

  - A rat presses a bar in its cage and receives a mild electrical shock on its feet. The shock is a negative condition for the rat. The rat presses the bar again and again receives a shock. The rat's behaviour of pressing the bar is weakened by the consequence of receiving a shock.

- In **Extinction** a particular behaviour is weakened by the consequence of not experiencing a positive condition or stopping a negative condition. For example:

  - A rat presses a bar in its cage and nothing happens. Neither a positive nor a negative condition exists for the rat. The rat presses the bar again, and again nothing happens. The rat's behaviour of pressing the bar is weakened by the consequence of not experiencing anything positive or stopping anything negative.

Learning occurs when the response is followed by a consequence that may be either a reinforcer or a punisher. The organism operates in its own environment and the behaviour is modified by its consequence.

## Application to Addictive Behaviour

Both the **positive** and the negative reinforcer are motivators to someone using a drug, in this case crack cocaine. For example, someone desires crack cocaine, they experience a 'high' after they use it and as a result this reinforces their tendency to want to use crack again, because they know that crack cocaine will give them that 'high'.

The **negative** reinforcer motivates the drug user, in this case the crack cocaine user. For example, because the crack cocaine user after experiencing a high knows that s/he will experience the 'horrible crash' after the 'high' they will use that negative experience to justify using the drug again and avoid the horrible crash.

Consequently, positive reinforcement directly rewards behaviour, e.g. disinhibition, social approval/acceptance. Negative reinforcement leads to avoidance of an unpleasant experience, e.g. relief of boredom, anxiety, relief of drug withdrawal symptoms. Adaptation/tolerance occurs so that larger doses are required to obtain the same effect.

**Punishment** is essentially the negative response to the behaviour someone is demonstrating. If that behaviour persists then the punishment persists. This carries on until the individual stops the behaviour. Services in many ways operate to this model, in direct and indirect ways. One particular service, which operates within this model would stereotypically be the Criminal Justice Service. Note: it is important to remember that many crack cocaine service users receive their initial introduction into treatment through the Criminal Justice Service.

**Extinction** from a treatment perspective, is how we might view a pharmacological intervention, i.e. through the process of giving someone a substitute drug, the crack cocaine service user would experience neither a positive nor negative sensation. The desire to use the drug would therefore diminish because the crack cocaine user would no longer experience any negative or positive sensations from using it.

Please note, there is currently no substitute medication for crack cocaine. Clearly what the advent of cocaine has brought to light for practitioners across the board in the drugs field, is the need for more highly developed, evidence based and well thought out non-pharmacological responses to cocaine use. The result could be one that benefits the whole drugs field, professionals and users alike. It could be argued that a holistic approach and the art of talking and using creative mediums to get the most for, and from, the service user has been lost over the years.

# Chapter Thirteen

## Confluence

Confluence is at the heart of what we do, it is the outcome that all professionals should strive towards, however, it is one that we rarely manage, even though it is at the heart of achieving and striving towards the best outcome for the service user.

**What is Confluence?**

Confluence is a term often referred to in geography. It describes the coming together of two or more bodies of water. It usually refers to where a tributary (i.e. a stream or minor river) joins a major river. A confluence is where two or more tributaries or rivers **flow together** or **come together to form one.** The idea of confluence is integral to the whole notion of providing a qualitative service to the crack cocaine user, because it could be argued that:

- Our understanding of the crack cocaine user is poor!
- Theoretical ideas associated with substance use are often blinkered and do not fully take into account the whole picture of the crack cocaine user.
- The way we work with crack cocaine is as much subjective as it is objective and evidence based.

- The counselling provision we offer crack cocaine service users is not well thought out.
- Services i.e. criminal justice services, voluntary services, hospital based services, community services etc. are fragmented.

While these issues remain collectively unexplored, there is no confluence.

There exists, probably a myth, that treatment for the crack cocaine user requires some special 'something.' i.e.:

- Some special form of pharmaco-therapy
- Some special form of specialised counselling
- Something special, special, special!

Treatment for all crack cocaine users or drug users per se, requires a humility that bypasses:

- Professional status
- Training
- Previous experience
- A professional's drug using history etc.

We constantly talk about teamwork, multi-disciplinary working, diversity, multi-organisational working. What we often do not talk about is why we do not work as well as we could with one another. This is applicable on a grand scale but it is no less applicable to the smaller scale i.e. the professional, the team and the service.

186

## Confluence and the Professional

*Confluence is in essence the conclusion to this discussion on engaging and working with crack cocaine service users, and in fact, with drug users as a whole. This discussion should hopefully provide a framework that allows the professional to better explore how they should employ their own skills and training to working with the crack cocaine user.*

*Is the crack cocaine service user any more complex to work with than the opiate, alcohol, or amphetamine user? In our experience - No! In fact, again in our experience, we have found quite the opposite to be true. Why might this be? Because in order to work effectively with the crack cocaine user one must employ interpersonal skills to engage, establish a rapport and build a relationship, just as with all other services users.*

*When we consider confluence, we need to allow our minds to expand with regards to how we normally think about crack cocaine treatment. It is very easy to talk about care pathways, partnership working etc, but what is the reality of these noble concepts and how often do we see them manifest to involve the service user and serve their actual best interests? Professionals and services for the crack cocaine service user are often complacent and essentially unimaginative. Imagination and creativity are almost seen as old-fashioned concepts in the present day world of good statistics that form the basis for 'evidence based research'. The former 'givens' of humanity, common sense, respect for individuality and un-harnessed imagination are often now seen as 'soft' options without theoretical foundation.*

## Confluence and the Service

Without an exploration of some of the issues raised in this book it may be counter-productive to try to develop services that might be accessed by crack cocaine users and ultimately benefit them in any meaningful way. There are many crack cocaine users in our communities who do not engage with services. Perhaps therefore, the barriers lay within the world of service provision rather than within the world of the crack cocaine user.

If we consider the treatment **tributaries:**

- Counselling interventions
- A suitable service environment
- Nutrition

How much attention might we give to each of these and how deeply do we look into our workforce and service to access the resources that might enable us to incorporate these elements in the service that we provide?

The following diagram illustrates what might need to be done in order to bring the aforementioned tributaries together to form **one.** The **'one'** in this case being the coordinated collaboration of the aspects of the service in order to respond effectively to the crack cocaine service user.

188

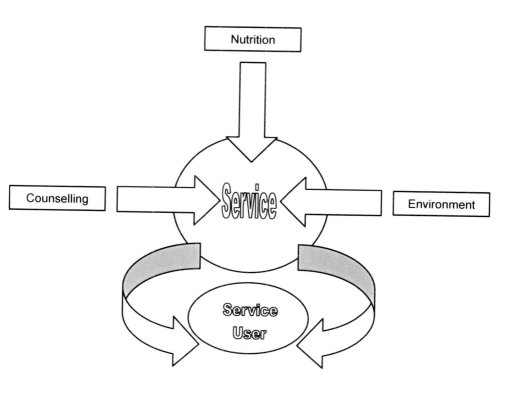

# Good treatment is very much like pharmaco-kinetics in that:

| Treatment: of the service user | Absorption: of interventions, ideas, health etc. | Excretion:

In this case refers to the best possible outcome for the service user |
| --- | --- | --- |
| | Distribution: of interventions throughout the organism | |
| | Metabolism: The reaction to all intervention within the organism at the same time | |

*Let us imagine a service user who requires:*

- Drug counselling
- Nutritional advice
- Health information
- 'Comfort' within the service environment
- A consistent message from a team of workers
- A drugs professional who understands their needs
- Clear boundaries

If the above represent pieces, they also present us with a puzzle. The challenge is to understand how each part is supposed to work and then how all the parts might fit together. When a worker sits with

190

a service user and draws up a care plan that is designed to address the users needs, there will often be a number of professionals identified to assist with their various specialisms. Such a plan looks impressive and sounds impressive, but how often are tasks simply carried forward from one care plan to the next, and how often might the service user be identified as the reason that the task has not been completed.

### An Image of Confluence!

- Take a painting palette
- Place two dollops of paint, one colour is red and the other blue
- On the palette the red and blue coloured paints are separate
- Mix the two colours together
- A new colour is created that has its own distinct nature
- It has become one
- That one is now **Purple**
- This is Confluence!

A great service has confluence, in which the service user, drugs professional, the team and the service environment operate well together. Creating a great service involves sacrifice. To become purple, blue has to sacrifice its status as blue and red has to sacrifice its status as red. We expect a certain amount of sacrifice from the service user and the same expectation necessarily applies to the drugs professional, the team and the umbrella organisation. To continue the metaphor, a skilled professional, like the skilled painter,

191

will be judicious and exercise discernment when planning an intervention or a new painting. S/he will make the best possible use of all resources, knowing when to sacrifice status and when to maintain it and take a lead role, or when to merge colours and when not. Confluence and harmony is achieved when all the constituent elements (services or colours) flow together in the best possible combination to create a service worthy of the service user or the painting.

# Conclusion

Unlike many books or discussions focusing on crack cocaine we have taken a slightly different position. We believe that change has to come from within, and that change is more than talking about the 'best' form of counselling for the crack cocaine service user and whether or not we should have complementary therapies within our services. This discussion is saying that many professionals recognise that the ethos, belief and the culture of how we work with this service user group has to be amended.

What is clear is that the knowledge and expertise is available to radically improve the quality of the provision we could offer this service user group as well as other service users. In order to do that we have to be able to discuss what is going on behind our own 'closed' and 'hidden' windows, and ask ourselves some searching, uncomfortable and thought-provoking questions. In this way a degree of confluence will be achieved and the journey for the whole drugs and related fields will be along a less bumpy road.

We hope that this brief excursion into how we have learned to work more effectively with crack cocaine users has made new connections between knowledge, theory and values for the reader. It was through our own experience and observations that we discovered that theory, policy and practice simply did not 'fit' and that the evidence pointed unavoidably to the fact that traditional models of intervention simply did not work for crack cocaine users. With some trepidation, but placing our trust in gut instinct, we wiped the slate clean, set aside all pre-conceptions and began to question the mismatch.

We wanted to cast our net wide so that we did not miss vital clues and so our first question was broad and general: 'Why are so many crack cocaine users not able to make the changes to their drug use which they originally asked us to help them with?' This led to further questions and simultaneously monitoring our commitment to exposing hidden assumptions and always sticking to facts to guide us to the next question the process unfolded.

The facts revealed that the service was created to employ trained professionals whose task was to assist self-referred drug users to manage their drug habit differently. We could find no discrepancy there, as all three elements were clearly in alignment. Theoretically, all three elements shared the same aims and objectives and should have resulted in satisfactory outcomes, but the facts showed all too clearly that these aims and objectives were not being achieved. We then refined our questions to dig deeper and asked: 'Was the service really created to help drug users to come off drugs? Are professionals genuinely committed to helping drug users reduce their habit and do they genuinely believe that it is possible? Are drug users genuine in their request for help? Our observations told us that the answer in all three elements had to be a 'yes'.

And so our dialogue with ourselves eventually uncovered the legacy of hidden assumptions and culture of despair endemic in the service, the professionals and the service users themselves. We realised that the map of service provision to drug users had some inherent

194

flaws despite the well intentioned motives of service providers, and although we all desired to reach the same destination, we needed to pack some different equipment, chart a new route and identify new landmarks.

This book is the result of our attempts to pack different equipment, chart a new route and plot some new landmarks that we have found helpful and that increase the likelihood of the fellow travellers (the service users, the professionals and the service) to journey with more optimism and encounter fewer dead ends. The map is by no means complete but we hope that it will open the door to more questions, new dimensions of discussion and ultimately to a service of which we can be justly proud and to which we have all contributed.

# Bibliography

**Allen D** (Ed) (1985): The Cocaine Crisis: Plenum Press.

**Blum K and Holder J M:** Handbook of Abusable Drugs. Garner Press Inc 1984 Journals

**Billberry J:** The Effective Manager, Perspective and Illustrations, Sage Publications, London, 1996

**Bonner A and Waterhouse J (ed):** Cognitive Behaviour Molecules to Mankind. MacMillan Press 1996

**Carroll K** (1998): A Cognitive Behavioural Approach: Treating Cocaine Addiction. US Department of Health & Human Services. National Institute of Health.

**Ciba Foundation Symposium 166:** Cocaine: Scientific and Social Dimensions
John Wiley and Sons 1992

**DeGruy Leary J (PHd):** Post Traumatic Slave Syndrome – 2005 Uptone Press. Milwaukie, Oregon

**Ditton J and Hammersley R** (1996): A Very Greedy Drug: Cocaine in Context: Harwood Academic Publishers.

**Edwards G and Littleton J (ed):** Pharmacological Treatments for Alcoholism. Mathuen Inc 1984

**Encyclopaedia Britannica (Edition 15)**

**Fisher S, Rasking A, Uhlenhuth** (Ed) (1987): Cocaine: Clinical and Bio-behavioural Aspects. Oxford University Press.

**Gold M S** (1993): Cocaine: Drugs of Abuse: A Comprehensive Series for Clinicians. Volume 3. Plenum Medical Book Company.

**Holder H D, Cisler R A, Longabaugh R, Stout R L, Treno A J & Zweben A.** (2000) Alcoholism treatment and medical care costs from Project MATCH. *Research Report.* Addiction 95 (7) 999-1013.

**Kang S Y, Kleinman P, Woody G, Millman R, Todd T, Kemp J, Lipton D:** Outcomes for Cocaine Abusers after Once-a-week Psychosocial Therapy: Am J Psychiatry 148:5, May 1991.

**Klee H** (Ed) Amphetamine Misuse: International Perspective on Current Trends. Hardwood Academic Publishers.

**Kouimtsidis C & Abou-Saleh M T** (1999) Psychological Treatment of Substance Misuse: A Review. The Arab Journal of Psychiatry Vol. 10 No. 2 Page (62-70).

**Lazear David** *Seven Ways of Knowing: Teaching for Multiple Intelligences* by. 1991. IRI/Skylight Publishing, Inc. Palatine, IL

**Leonard B E:** Fundamental of Psycho-pharmacology (2nd Editon) John Wiley and Sons 1996

**Levine H & Reinarman C** (2002) Crack in the Rear View Mirror: Deconstructing Drug War Mythology

**Lingford-Hughes A R et al**
Reduced Levels of GABA-benzodiazepine receptor in alcohol dependency
in the absence of grey matter atrophy British Journal of Psychiatry 1998. 173, 116-122

**Ling-ford Hughes A R et al:** Levels of gamma-amino butyric acid-benzodiazepine receptors in abstinence, alcohol dependent women.

**Marlatt A and Vandenbos G** (Ed) (1997): Addictive Behaviours: Reading on Etiology, Prevention and Treatment. American Psychological Association.

**NIDA's** (1999): Psychosocial treatments for Cocaine Dependence: US Department of Health & Human Services. National Institute of Health.

**Platt J J:** Cocaine Addiction Theory, research and treatment. Harvard University Press 1997

**Rogers Carl R.** Way of Being. Boston: Houghton Mifflin, 1980

**Seivewright N A and Greenwood J** (1996): What is important in drug misuse treatment. Lancet, 347: 373-376.

**Skinner B F:** About Behaviourism. Random House Inc. 1974

**Volkow et al** (1999): Association of Methylphenidate -Induced Craving With Changes in Right Striato-orbital Metabolism in Cocaine Abusers: Am J Psychiatry156:1 January.

**Wallace B C (Ph.D):**
Crack Cocaine A Practical Treatment Approach for the Chemically Dependent
Brunner/Mazel Inc1990

**Washton A M** (1989) Cocaine Addiction Treatment & Relapse Prevention. A Norton Professional Book. New York.

http://www.wikipedia.com
http://www.nida.com